CHALLENGER 5

ADULT READING SERIES

COREA
MURPHY

NEW READERS PRESS

About the Author

Corea Murphy has worked in the field of education since the early 1960s. In addition to classroom and tutorial teaching, Ms. Murphy has developed language arts curriculum guides for public high schools, conducted curriculum and effectiveness workshops, and established an educational program for residents in a drug rehabilitation facility.

Ms. Murphy became interested in creating a reading series for older students when she began working with adults and adolescents in the early 1970s. The **Challenger Adult Reading Series** is the result of her work with these students.

In a very real sense, the students contributed greatly to the development of this reading series. Their enthusiasm for learning to read and their willingness to work hard provided inspiration, and their many helpful suggestions influenced the content of both the student books and the teacher's manuals.

It is to these students that the **Challenger Adult Reading Series** is dedicated with the hope that others who wish to become good readers will find this reading program both helpful and stimulating.

A special note of gratitude is also extended to Kay Koschnick, Christina Jagger, and Mary Hutchison of New Readers Press for their work and support in guiding this series to completion.

Every effort has been made to locate the heirs of Else Zentner and Henri Duvernois to obtain permission to reprint their stories, respectively, "How Grandpa Came into Money" and "Clothes Make the Man." If the heirs are located subsequent to publication, they are hereby entitled to due compensation.

ISBN 0-88336-785-8

© 1985
New Readers Press
Division of ProLiteracy Worldwide
1320 Jamesville Ave., Syracuse, New York 13210

Printed in the United States of America

Designed by Chris Steenwerth
Cover by Chris Steenwerth

Cover photo by Royce Bair/The Stock Solution

Table of Contents

Lesson 1

Review of Long and Short Vowels

ā	daze	haze	hazy	mane	gape	ă	taxi	ban	vast	rap	gap
ē	equal	equally	zebra	decoy reorder	he's	ě	pencil	wept	vent	vet veteran	veterinarian
ī	Nile	rind	lion	license	arise	ĭ	quiz	wick	inner	jig	jiggle
ō	solo	obey	disobey	yoke	arose	ŏ	odds	bother	bonnet	cotton contest	
ū	ruby	Susan	humor	humorous humid		ŭ	mutt	fuzz	cuss	custard mustard	

1 **Word Meanings.** Use the words at the left to fill in the blanks.

ban
decoy
gap
gape
jiggle
mane
mutt
Nile
rind
vast
veterinarian
yoke

_____ 1. a crossbar with two U-shaped pieces that go around the necks of a pair of oxen, mules, or other animals working in a team

_____ 2. a dog of mixed breeding

_____ 3. a living or fake bird or other animal which hunters use to draw game into a trap or within shooting range

_____ 4. a person who is trained and licensed to treat animals

_____ 5. a tough outer covering, such as the skin of some fruits

_____ 6. an opening; a break or pass through the mountains

_____ 7. huge in size, number, degree, etc.

_____ 8. the long hair along the top and sides of the neck of such mammals as the horse and the male lion

_____ 9. the longest river in Africa (more than 4,000 miles)

_____ 10. to forbid something

_____ 11. to open the mouth wide; to yawn; to stare at

_____ 12. to move or rock lightly

Words for Study

grandpa	train wreck	castor oil	welcome
somewhere	meantime	carefully	granddaughter
earnings	stretchers	insurance	following

How Grandpa Came into Money

He was a sweet man, my grandfather, but when the brains were passed out he must have been somewhere else. I still respect how Grandmother could raise a family on his earnings.

Perhaps you can understand what it meant when, one fine day, Lady Luck smiled on Grandfather. He got himself in a train wreck.

Now, if something like that happened to you (and you lived through it) you had it made. The railroad would pay. So all of the lucky people on the train knew exactly what to do: they began to groan loudly and twist about on the ground while waiting for the doctors and stretchers to come.

All but Grandfather!

Never in his life had he missed a meal and he was not going to start now. No sir! Not for a little trainwreck. So he cut himself a walking stick and set out for home—a three hour walk.

In the meantime, the news of the wreck had already reached our town and the news had reported, "No deaths."

I cannot describe the many looks that passed across my grandmother's face when she saw her husband come strolling in the door, covered with dust, a bit tired from his long walk, but safe and smiling for he was just in time for dinner. First came joy at seeing that her man was not hurt. Then the joy turned into anger.

Grandfather had passed up his one and only golden chance.

So Grandmother turned into a kind of wild storm. Before he knew what was happening, he found himself without his pants and in bed. His complaints did him no good. Grandmother slapped a wet towel on his head while Mother went to search for the only medicine we had in the house—castor oil!

Grandfather cried out in fear and tried to hide under the blanket, but Mother dosed him anyway. Poor man! The only thing he really needed was his dinner. But what could he or anyone else do once his wife and daughter had made up their minds.

And then came the time of waiting. The two women did all they could do to keep Grandpa in bed and coached him carefully on what to say when the railroad people came. Grandpa nodded and said he would do as he was told. However, he bribed one of us children to find his pants for him and got out of bed anyway.

And out of bed he was when the insurance people from the railroad came to our town. Pants, boots, and all, grandpa was stuffed into bed and the covers were pulled up to his chin. The shades were lowered, the castor oil was placed by his bed, and the insurance people were brought in.

From the first minute it was clear that Grandpa had forgotten all of the careful coaching. He beamed a welcome to the insurance people and told them how well they looked. He then went on to talk about the weather and crops. When the railroad doctor was able to get a word in and asked him what injuries he had gotten in the train wreck, my grandfather smiled and said, "There's really nothing at all wrong with me that 100,000 dollars couldn't cure."

Mother promptly fainted. Grandmother screamed and ran out of the room. The insurance men doubled up with laughter.

After they had stopped laughing and revived my poor mother, the insurance men gave Grandpa 5,000 dollars—making him the richest man in our little town.

But to his dying day, Grandpa could never understand why the insurance men had given him the money.

Adapted from "How Grandpa Came into Money" by Else Zentner.

2 **About the Story.** Choose the best answer from the four choices and write it on the line.

1. Who is telling the story in "How Grandpa Came into Money"? _____
   - (a) Grandpa
   - (b) Mother
   - (c) the granddaughter
   - (d) the grandmother

2. What does Grandpa seem to like best? _____
   - (a) farming
   - (b) food
   - (c) money
   - (d) train rides

3. The other people on the train were _____.
   - (a) badly injured
   - (b) faking injuries
   - (c) in a state of shock
   - (d) killed

4. The grandmother's *first* feeling when she sees Grandpa coming in the door is _____.
   - (a) calm
   - (b) happiness
   - (c) rage
   - (d) sadness

5. Grandpa is given castor oil because _____.
   - (a) Grandmother is angry with him
   - (b) he is ill from the train wreck
   - (c) he needs a little castor oil now and then
   - (d) there is no other medicine to give him

6. When the insurance men come to the house, _____.
   - (a) Grandpa is being given a dose of castor oil
   - (b) Grandpa is eating dinner
   - (c) Grandpa is nude
   - (d) Grandpa isn't where he's supposed to be

7. Which of the following is *not* part of Grandmother's plan to convince the insurance men that

   Grandpa has been injured in the train wreck? _____
   - (a) She lowers the shades.
   - (b) She pulls up the covers.
   - (c) She puts Grandpa in bed with his clothes on.
   - (d) She puts castor oil by his bed.

8. When Grandpa answers the insurance men's questions about his injuries, the men

   are _____.
   - (a) amused
   - (b) angry
   - (c) confused
   - (d) disgusted

9. Why did the insurance men give Grandpa the money? _____
   - (a) He has such an awful wife.
   - (b) He needs it.
   - (c) He is so humorous.
   - (d) We don't really know why.

10. The family in this story lives _____.
   - (a) in a city
   - (b) in a town
   - (c) on a farm
   - (d) on an island

3 **Which Word Does Not Fit?** Choose the word that does not fit with the rest and write it on the line.

1.	ketchup	mustard	pickles	picnic	_____
2.	dentist	doctor	veteran	veterinarian	_____
3.	diamond	jewelry	pearl	ruby	_____
4.	damp	drenched	humid	muggy	_____
5.	cried	groaned	sobbed	wept	_____
6.	bicycle	bus	subway	taxi	_____
7.	huge	immense	vast	wonderful	_____
8.	earnings	expenses	income	wages	_____
9.	bother	fuss	humor	trouble	_____
10.	amusing	foolish	funny	humorous	_____
11.	expose	protect	reveal	show	_____
12.	edgy	gloomy	nervous	tense	_____
13.	comply	follow	obey	reply	_____
14.	pit	rind	seed	stone	_____
15.	cautious	cloudy	confused	hazy	_____

4 **Grandpa Celebrates His Good Luck.** Form compound words by using a word from **List A** and adding a word from **List B** to it. Use these compound words to complete the sentences. Study the example before you begin.

List A	List B
bath	bags
blue	berry
butter	√headed
coffee	house
√light	milk
mad	paper
meal	pie
money	pot
news	robe
pot	time

1. When Grandpa was given $5,000 by the insurance men, the family was so excited that they felt _lightheaded_.

2. All the singing and shouting turned their quiet little home into a _____.

3. The first one to come to his senses was Grandpa himself, for the growling in his stomach told him it was _____.

4. Grandmother cheerfully gave him a piece of _____ pie to snack on so that he wouldn't bother her with complaints while she fixed dinner.

5. "Where is the _____?" asked Grandpa. "You know I always like a big glass of it with my pie."

6. "Listen to Mr. _____!" exclaimed Grandmother. "He's been rich for almost one whole hour, and he's already hard to live with!"

7. "Just pretend he's not here," said Mother as she filled her cup from the pretty yellow _____ I had given her for her birthday.

8. As Grandmother cut up the chicken for the _____ she was going to bake for dinner, Grandpa ate his pie and dreamed about how he would spend the money.

9. "I know what I'll buy!" he declared. "I'm going to buy a new _____."

10. Then when the _____ reporters want to talk to me after my next train wreck, I'll be all set to have my picture taken.

Lesson 2

Review of Consonant Blends and Digraphs: Part 1

ch		sh		st	
champ	ranch	sh!	marsh	stab	crest
chant	beech	shall	marshy	stack	yeast
chap	stench	shoe	marshmallow	stag	roost
chapel	clinch	shed	slash	stagger	rooster
cherry	hitch	shabby	slosh	steeple	host
chock	hutch	shipshape	galoshes	stiff	ghost
childish	snitch	shiver	wishbone	stole	outburst
chuckle	torch	shudder	wishy-washy	stub	haste

1 **Word Meanings.** Use the words at the left to fill in the blanks.

chapel
chuckle
host
marshmallow
shabby
shipshape
snitch
stag
stench
torch
wishy-washy
yeast

_____ 1. Many people like to put this in their hot chocolate to make it taste sweeter.

_____ 2. This is a long piece of wood with a flame on one end.

_____ 3. This is a party for men only.

_____ 4. This is what you call the person who gives a party and makes sure the guests are having a good time.

_____ 5. This slang word means to tell on someone.

_____ 6. This is a soft laugh.

_____ 7. This is a place where people can pray. It is smaller than a church.

_____ 8. This is used by bakers. It makes dough rise.

_____ 9. This word describes a person who has a lot of trouble making up his mind about what he ought to do.

_____ 10. This word describes a smell that is so awful that people often have to hold their breaths to keep from gagging.

_____ 11. This word describes having everything exactly in place.

_____ 12. This word describes something that is broken down or worn out.

Words for Study

Midas	grant	joyfully	reaction
Bacchus	petals	doubt	shortchange
power	palace	deathly	synonym

The Greed for Gold

"Nothing," according to an old saying, "can ever make a greedy man happy." The saying is proved by the story of King Midas.

Once, long ago, some farmers found a man sleeping in their fields. The man felt he had every right to be there—after all, he was the god of wine, and he had been drinking. His hair was matted, his clothes were dirty, and he looked like some kind of tramp. The farmers bound his wrists and brought him to Midas, their king. Midas knew who he was at once.

"Untie his hands," Midas commanded. "This is no common person. This is Bacchus, the Greek god who blesses your vines, who sees that the sun makes your grapes ripe and gives you good crops."

The king not only saved Bacchus, but gave parties in his honor for weeks. At the end of the time Bacchus said, "It is within my power to grant any desire you may have. What would you wish for most?"

Midas was a very rich man, but being greedy, he felt he was not nearly rich enough. He did not even pause, but said at once, "I wish that everything I touch would turn to gold."

"It is a strange wish," said Bacchus. "But it is granted. No matter what you touch, it will become gold at once."

Midas was delighted. He began to test Bacchus's words to see if they were really true. He broke off a branch from a tree, and the stem and gray leaves became a golden spray. He picked up a small stone, and it changed into a little ball of gold. He put a finger on a rose and its petals were heavy with gold. He went from tree to tree, touching and turning them into a stiff, solid gold forest. He put his palm against his palace walls, and his palace burned with a golden glow.

Joyfully he ordered a huge meal and sat down to enjoy it. The glass became gold at once, and as soon as his lips touched the wine, he choked. What went into his mouth was not a liquid but hard gold—worth a great deal no doubt but hardly something to drink. It was the same with the food. The peas were tiny golden balls in his mouth. The meat would have broken his teeth had he tried to chew it. He staggered from the table.

"I shall starve!" he cried. "The gift was not a blessing but a curse! I shall be killed with gold!"

Scared, King Midas sought Bacchus. "Help me!" he cried. "If you do not, I shall die."

"What troubles you so?" asked Bacchus.

"Your gift," said Midas with anger in his voice. "No one can eat or drink gold!"

Bacchus smiled. "I thought you would tire of the golden touch. It is often sad not to get everything you wish, but it is sometimes sadder to get it. If you want to get rid of the power, go to the river. Wash your body in the deepest part of the stream. The sands will change into gold, but you will be clean and free of the deathly charm."

Once cured, Midas hated the sight of gold. He turned away from all shows of riches and went to live in the woods where he became a follower of another god, Pan, who was the god of the flocks, fields, and forests.

Adapted from *The Firebringer and Other Great Stories* by Louis Untermeyer. Copyright © 1968 by Louis Untermeyer. Reprinted by permission of the publisher, M. Evans and Co. Inc. New York, New York.

2 **About the Story.** Answer the following questions according to the story you have just read.

1. In Greek stories, Bacchus is the god of _____.

2. In Greek stories, Pan is the god of _____.

3. When Midas sees that everything he touches turns to gold, his first reaction is _____

_____.

4. What causes Midas to change his mind about wanting gold?

_____

5. Match the causes with the right effects and write your answers on the lines below.
    Because Bacchus grants him his wish,
    Because Bacchus is a god,
    Because Bacchus looks so dirty,
    Because Midas is greedy,
    Because Midas hates gold,

Cause	Effect
a. _____	everything Midas touches turns to gold.
b. _____	he becomes a follower of Pan.
c. _____	he makes the wish that he does.
d. _____	King Midas gives a lot of parties for him.
e. _____	the farmers drag him to King Midas.

6. If you met Bacchus and he told you he would grant any wish you asked for, what would your wish be? (Be sure to answer this question in good sentence form.)

_____

_____

3 **Strange Sentences.** Put the words at the left in the blanks so the sentences make sense.

changed
Charles's
cheesecake
chocolate
choice

1. _____ first _____ for dessert was

a piece of _____ _____, but then he

_____ his mind.

chairman
cheapskate
checkbook
chess

2. The _____ of the _____ club was such

a _____ that he left his _____ at home

wherever he went.

shed
shelf
shiny
shotgun
shoved

3. The murderer _____ the _____ _____

to the back of the _____ in the _____.

she
shortchanged
shortstop
show
shy

4. The _____ was so _____ that he didn't have the nerve to

_____ the waitress how _____ had _____ him.

States
strange
student
studying
stuff

5. As the _____ was _____ the history of the

United _____, he thought to himself: "This is _____

_____."

stage
stage fright
staggered
stairway
standstill
step

6. The actor had such a bad case of _____ that he missed

a _____ on the _____, _____ for

a moment and then fell onto the _____, and brought the play

to a complete _____.

4 **Working with Synonyms.** A *synonym* is a word that means the same or nearly the same as another word. Choose the word in each line that is a synonym for the first word and write it to the right. Study the example before you begin.

1. **crest:**	bottom	middle	side	top	_top_
2. **childish:**	childhood	little	silly	cheerful	
3. **welcome:**	chat	greet	hello	party	
4. **shipshape:**	messy	neat	ocean	sailor	
5. **champ:**	boxer	fighter	sport	winner	
6. **shiver:**	shame	shout	shrink	shudder	
7. **stench:**	smell	sight	stink	taste	
8. **snatch:**	snip	squeal	steal	steel	
9. **gag:**	chew	choke	digest	swallow	
10. **shabby:**	greasy	sloppy	ugly	worn-out	
11. **gape:**	chuckle	spout	stare	wonder	
12. **dazed:**	confused	exhausted	jumpy	threatened	

Lesson 3

Review of Consonant Blends: Part 2

bl:	blaze	blab	blessed	blimp	blond(e)	blur	blubber
br:	brat	breach	brittle	brim	brighten	broth	brushoff
cl:	clamp	cleat	cling	clot	clove	clover	clump
cr:	craft	cram	crank	creak	creaky	cripple	cruel
fl:	flatter	flattery	flex	flick	floss	flown	flung
fr:	fraction	fret	fringe	fro	frost	frosting	frostbite

1 **Word Meanings.** Use the words at the left to fill in the blanks.

blubber
blur
brittle
cleat
cling
clover
cruel
flatter
flattery
fraction
fro
frostbite

_____ 1. You might say this to a person who has just said something nice to you: "_____ will get you nowhere."

_____ 2. Something that is likely to break because it is hard and dry and cannot be stretched is regarded as _____.

_____ 3. This piece of iron on a football player's shoe helps the foot to grip the ground.

_____ 4. This plant has many leaves and small flowers. (If you're lucky, you find one that has four leaves!)

_____ 5. This injury to the tissues in the body is caused by being exposed to extreme cold.

_____ 6. This is the thick layer of fat between the skin and the muscle layers of whales and other sea mammals.

_____ 7. This word describes someone who causes others pain and suffering.

_____ 8. This word means to praise somebody in a phony way.

_____ 9. This word means a part of something.

_____ 10. When you hold on or remain close to something, you _____ to it.

_____ 11. When you smear or smudge something so it can't be seen very well, you _____ it.

_____ 12. When you swing something back and forth, you are swinging it to and _____.

Words for Study

Tango	Paris	panhandled	whisper
partner	intelligent	saluted	whistle
uniform	half-wit	madam	arrest

Clothes Make the Man

"I don't like it," Tango complained again. "I won't feel right, walking up and down in that."

"Shut up and put it on," the Boss told him, and so, of course, Tango put it on. The Boss was half the size of Tango, but he was smart. If they had given Tango a tail, he would have put it between his legs when the Boss spoke.

"Not bad," Tango had to admit, looking at himself in the mirror. He pushed out his mighty chest and threw back his huge shoulders. Even the Eel, who was the Boss's working partner and who rarely opened his mouth, was stirred to speech. "Boy, he *is* handsome!" he said.

No question about it, Tango looked good. The policeman's uniform might have been made by the best tailor in Paris. His little eyes looked brighter under the cap; they almost looked intelligent.

"Stop staring at yourself and wipe that dumb grin off your face," the Boss said, "and listen. This is so easy a half-wit could do it, so maybe if you try hard, you can too. All you do is walk up and down the street. Easy and slow, like a real cop on his beat. Then if anybody hears us working in the house, they won't start asking questions. Keep walking until we come out, then hang around a few minutes covering us. That's all there is to it. Now, you understand?"

"Sure," Tango said, his eyes straying to the mirror.

"Then get going!" the Boss snapped.

Tango was a little edgy walking to the street the Boss and the Eel had picked out, but nothing happened. The house where the job was to be pulled was in the middle of the block. Tango had rarely seen a street such as this one because he worked in the shabby quarters of Paris—a little purse-snatching, a little shoplifting; he even panhandled.

He strolled down the sidewalk, turned at the corner, and came back. While he was turning at the other corner, he saw the police officer. Such a sight would normally send him off as fast as his feet would move. He stared in fear; his palms were sweating. Then, with the officer a few feet from him, he raised his arm and saluted.

The officer calmly returned the salute and passed by.

Tango stood peering after him. He felt strange and thankful. "Say!" he said to himself. "Say, you see that? I salute him, and he salutes right back. I guess I look good to him," he told himself. "I guess he don't see many cops looking so good."

After a few more trips, he found an old lady pausing on the corner. Tango did not even see the fat purse in her hand. He stopped in front of her, saluted, and offered his arm. She looked at him with a sweet smile. "Oh, thank you, officer!"

"Please, madam," Tango said, "don't say a word." He paused. "That's what we're here for," he added and saluted her with pride.

A shabby man then came toward him. As he spotted Tango, he growled. "Rotten cop!" he cried. "Big bag of wind in a uniform! I spit on you!" the drunk declared. And he spit on Tango.

Something popped in Tango's head. He grabbed the drunk with one mighty hand and dragged him off down the street. When the Boss and the Eel returned from completing the job, Tango was in no mood to stop.

"You fool, what are you doing?" the Boss asked in an angry whisper. "You want to spoil the whole job?" And he struck Tango hard across the cheek.

Feelings that can't be described swirled in Tango's head. He remembered the officer answering his salute; he remembered the old lady's sweet smile. And then he remembered what the drunk had said.

He rose to the full pitch of a mighty anger.

While the Boss and the Eel stared at him in sheer fright, Tango stuffed the shiny police whistle in his mouth and blew loud and long enough to bring all the police in Paris.

"Crooks, robbers!" he roared. "I arrest you! I arrest you in the name of the law!"

Adapted from "Clothes Make the Man" by Henri Duvernois.

2 **About the Story.** Choose the answer that best completes the sentence and write it on the line.

1. The Boss had probably wanted Tango for this job because he is _____.

   (a) good-looking   (c) intelligent
   (b) huge   (d) quick

2. Based on his name, the Boss had probably wanted the Eel for this job because he

   is _____.

   (a) good-looking   (c) intelligent
   (b) huge   (d) quick

3. When Tango first begins to walk up and down the street in his uniform, he

   is _____.

   (a) helpful   (c) proud
   (b) nasty   (d) tense

4. The first one to cause Tango to feel better about himself is the _____.

   (a) drunk   (c) old lady
   (b) Eel   (d) police officer

5. The job that the three men are doing is _____.

   (a) holding up a bank   (c) robbing a house
   (b) mugging an old lady   (d) rolling a drunk

6. When the Boss sees Tango with the drunk, he is _____.

   (a) amused   (c) calm
   (b) angry   (d) flattered

7. Tango blows the whistle on the Boss and the Eel _____

   _____.

   (a) because he hopes the judge will let him off lightly   (c) because he wants to get even with them
   (b) because he really believes he is an officer   (d) by mistake

8. "Clothes make the man" means that _____

_____ .

   (a) people should have as many clothes as they can
   (b) people trust men in a policeman's uniform
   (c) what you wear affects how you feel about yourself
   (d) you can't walk around in the nude

9. Paris is located in _____ .

   (a) England   (c) Italy
   (b) France   (d) Spain

10. The word *tango* is also the name of a _____ .

   (a) clown   (c) fruit
   (b) dance   (d) policeman

What do you think? If you had a job in which you had to wear a uniform, and your boss told you that you could wear any kind of uniform you wanted, what would your uniform look like? Use as many details as you can to describe your uniform.

_____

_____

_____

_____

3 **More Strange Sentences.** Put the words at the left in the blanks so the sentences make sense.

black
blind
blonde
blurted
blushed

1. The _____ in the _____ dress _____

   when her boyfriend _____ out how beautiful she was

   to the _____ man.

clammy
Clark's
clerk
clip
cloth

2. On Ms. _____ first day as a _____ , her hands were

   so _____ that she couldn't _____ the price tags off

   the _____ properly.

crammed
cramps
crates
crawl
crouched

3. The little boy _____ behind the fruit _____ and

   _____ so many peaches and plums down his throat that he ended up

   with a bad case of stomach _____ and had to _____ home.

flashlights
flickering
floated
flooded
flung

4. When the lights started _____ in the _____ town, the people _____ their belongings on rafts and, guided by their _____, _____ to safety.

freaked
Fred
freeway
Friday
frightened

5. _____ hated to ride with Butch, who was so _____ of the _____ that he _____ out whenever he had to drive during the _____ rush hour.

brand-new
breadbox
bribed
bride
broke
brother's

6. The _____ _____ her _____ _____ over her _____ head when she learned that the groom had been _____ to marry her.

4 **Synonyms.** Match each word at the left with its synonym. Study the example before you begin.

ban
fret
fringe
frosting
haste
marsh
√panhandle
power
roost
salute
slash
snitch

panhandle   1. beg

_____   2. cut

_____   3. edge

_____   4. forbid

_____   5. greet

_____   6. hurry

_____   7. icing

_____   8. perch

_____   9. steal or blab

_____   10. strength

_____   11. swamp

_____   12. worry

5 **Which Word Fits Best?** Fill in each blank with the word that best completes the sentence.

1. Cleat is to football as mouthpiece is to _____.
   (a) boxing   (b) checkers   (c) Ping-Pong   (d) tennis

2. Bottle is to wine as _____ is to salt.
   (a) bowl   (b) food   (c) pepper   (d) shaker

3. Outburst is to sound as stench is to _____.
   (a) hearing   (b) sight   (c) smell   (d) taste   (e) touch

4. Sloppy is to shipshape as wishy-washy is to _____.
   (a) certain   (b) dirty   (c) unsafe   (d) unsure

5. Marshmallow is to sweet as clove is to _____.
   (a) ham   (b) spicy   (c) sugar   (d) sugarless

6. Wishbone is to _____ as claws are to lobster.
   (a) chicken   (b) dressing   (c) Thanksgiving   (d) wishes

7. Wise is to foolish as _____ is to cruel.
   (a) fret   (b) kindhearted   (c) stiff   (d) wishy-washy

8. Power is to lack of force as _____ is to weakness.
   (a) energy   (b) health   (c) muscles   (d) strength

9. Accident is to train wreck as crime is to _____.
   (a) arresting   (b) panhandling   (c) shoplifting   (d) shortchanging

10. Cabbage is to salad as _____ is to stew.
    (a) apple   (b) beef   (c) egg   (d) vanilla

Lesson 4

Review of Consonant Blends: Part 3

gl:	glaze	glassful	Glen	glider	glittery	glob	glum
gr:	grate	grateful	grandson	Greenland	grim	grope	grubby
pl:	planter	placement	pleasure	pliers	plop	pluck	plumber
pr:	prank	pressure	prime	princess	prod	prowl	prowler
sl:	slate	slack	slime	slimy	slit	slope	slug
str:	strangle	strangler	strep	strengthen	stride	strive	strut

1 **Word Meanings.** Choose a word at the left that is a synonym for or example of the items listed below. Study the example before you begin.

Group A

Glen

√ Greenland

pliers

plumber

prime

princess

slug

strangle

stride

strive

Greenland   1. a country near the North Pole

_____ 2. a man's name

_____ 3. a tool used for holding, bending, or cutting

_____ 4. first-rate

_____ 5. a person who fixes leaky pipes and clogged drains

_____ 6. the king's daughter

_____ 7. to choke

_____ 8. to put a great deal of energy into something; to struggle

_____ 9. to take long steps while walking

_____ 10. used instead of a coin in a machine

Group B

glittery
glum
grateful
grope
grubby
prank
prowl
prowler
slack
slope

_____ 1. a trick (sometimes not a very nice one)

_____ 2. dirty; messy

_____ 3. downhearted; gloomy

_____ 4. shiny

_____ 5. slant

_____ 6. slow; not busy; loose; not tight

_____ 7. thankful

_____ 8. a person who searches in a sneaky way for someone
to attack

_____ 9. to haunt or search in a sneaky way for someone to attack

_____ 10. to search about blindly for something

Words for Study

avenue	eyebrow	enlarged	steady
unlighted	Jimmy	interest	plainclothes man
keen	grasp	Chicago	antonym

After Twenty Years

The policeman on the beat moved up the avenue. The time was barely ten o'clock at night, but chilly gusts of wind with a taste of rain in them had forced most of the people indoors.

When about to the middle of a certain block, the policeman suddenly slowed his walk. In the doorway of a hardware store a man leaned with an unlighted cigar in his mouth. As the policeman walked up to him, the man spoke up quickly.

"It's all right, officer," he said. "I'm just waiting for a friend. It's a date made twenty years ago. Sounds a little funny to you, doesn't it? Well, I'll explain if you'd like to make certain it's all right. About that long ago there used to be a restaurant where this store stands."

"Until five years ago," said the policeman. "It was torn down then."

The man in the doorway struck a match and lit his cigar. The light showed a pale face with keen eyes and a little white scar near his right eyebrow.

"Twenty years ago tonight," said the man, "I dined here with Jimmy Wells, my best friend and the greatest guy in the world. The next morning I was to start for the West to strike it rich. You couldn't have dragged Jimmy out of New York. Well, we agreed that night that we would meet here again exactly twenty years from that date and time no matter what."

"Did pretty well out West, didn't you?" asked the policeman as he watched the man pull out a handsome watch, the lids of it set with small diamonds.

"You bet! I hope Jimmy has done half as well."

The policeman took a step or two. "I'll be on my way. Going to call time on him sharp?"

"I should say not!" said the other. "I'll give him half an hour at least. If Jimmy is alive on earth, he'll be here by that time."

"Hope your friend comes around all right. Good night, sir," said the policeman passing on along his beat trying the doors as he went.

The man waited about twenty minutes, and then a tall man in a long overcoat hurried across from the other side of the street. He went right up to the waiting man.

"Is that you, Bob?" he asked with a note of doubt in his voice.

"Is that you, Jimmy Wells?" cried the man in the door.

"Bless my heart!" exclaimed the second man, grasping both the other's hands with his own. "It's Bob, sure as fate. Well, well, well—twenty years is a long time. The old restaurant's gone, Bob. I wish it had lasted, so we could have another dinner there. How has the West treated you?"

"It has given me everything I asked for. You've changed a lot, Jimmy. I never thought you were so tall."

"Oh, I grew a bit after I was twenty."

"Doing well in New York, Jimmy?"

"I'm okay. I have a job with the city. Come on, Bob. We'll go around to a place I know of and have a good long talk about the old times."

The two men started up the avenue, arm in arm. The man from the West, his pride enlarged by success, was beginning to outline the history of his life. The other listened with interest.

At the corner stood a drugstore, bright with lights. When they came into this glare, each of them turned at the same time to gaze upon the other's face.

The man from the West stopped suddenly and released his arm.

"You're not Jimmy Wells," he snapped. "Twenty years is a long time, but not long enough to change the shape of a man's nose."

"It sometimes changes a good man into a bad one," said the tall man. "You've been under arrest for ten minutes, 'Silky' Bob. Chicago thinks you may have dropped over our way and wires us she wants to have a chat with you. Going calmly, aren't you? That makes sense. Now, before we go, here's a note. It's from Officer Wells.

The man from the West opened the little piece of paper. His hand was steady when he began to read, but it shook a little by the time he had read it through. The note was short:

Bob: I was at the agreed place on time. When you struck the match to light your cigar, I saw it was the face of the man wanted in Chicago. I just couldn't do it myself, so I went around and got a plainclothes man to do the job.

Jimmy

Adapted from "After Twenty Years" by O. Henry with permission of Airmont Publishing Company, Inc. New York, New York.

2 **About the Story.** Answer these questions.

1. True or false? If the statement is true, write *true* on the line. If the statement is false, write *false* AND make the statement true by putting the right word or words above the part of the statement that is false. Study the example before you begin.

false   a. "After Twenty Years" takes place in the ~~West.~~ *East.*

_____ b. Jimmy Wells is a police officer.

_____ c. The avenue on which 'Silky' Bob waits for his friend is quite crowded.

_____ d. 'Silky' Bob smokes cigars.

_____ e. 'Silky' Bob hasn't seen Jimmy for five years.

_____ f. The two men meet each other in front of a restaurant.

_____ g. 'Silky' Bob first sees the other man's face in front of a hardware store.

_____ h. 'Silky' Bob knows the man isn't Jimmy because he is so tall.

_____ i. 'Silky' Bob is wanted by the police in Baltimore.

_____ j. The man who arrests 'Silky' Bob isn't wearing a uniform.

_____ k. 'Silky' Bob finds out Jimmy Wells is the policeman only because the plainclothes man tells him.

_____ l. Jimmy Wells has always wanted to live in the West.

2. If you were Jimmy Wells in this story, what would you have done? Be sure to give reasons for your answer.

_____

_____

_____

3 **Working with Antonyms.** An *antonym* is a word that means the opposite or nearly the opposite of another word. Match the words at the left with their antonyms. Study the example before you begin.

antonym
arrest
cheapskate
comply
enlarge
√first-rate
follower
half-wit
host
shortchanged
steady
strength

first-rate   1. awful

_____ 2. disobey

_____ 3. egghead

_____ 4. guest

_____ 5. leader

_____ 6. overpaid

_____ 7. release

_____ 8. shaky

_____ 9. shrink

_____ 10. spendthrift

_____ 11. synonym

_____ 12. weakness

4 **Strange Verses.** Put the words at the left in the blanks so the verses make sense.

blurred
clink
drink
glasses
slurred
think

At the party, all the _____ did _____.

Then one of the guests began to _____ :

"My speech is quite _____ ,

Everything looks _____ .

I think I shall throw out this _____ ."

distress
dress
flabby
princess
shabby
squeeze

There once was a fat, young _____ ,

Who was in such a state of _____ .

Her palace was _____ ,

And she herself was so _____

That she couldn't _____ into her _____ .

crippled
dread
fled
frightened
prowler
snatching

As a _____ was _____ her purse,

The _____ little lady did curse.

She filled him with _____,

And, _____, he _____,

Yelling, "How can life get any worse!"

5 **Compound Words.** To find the answers to these questions, choose a word from List A and add a word from List B to it. Study the example before you begin.

List A	List B
√butter	blind
blow	bound
color	√fly
grand	handle
head	house
pan	lash
pay	line
play	pen
power	roll
spell	stand
spend	thrift
whip	torch

butterfly   1. an insect some people collect

_____ 2. a person who has great force or energy

_____ 3. a roofed stand for people who are watching a game, concert, etc.

_____ 4. at the top of the first page of a newspaper

_____ 5. he spends his money as fast as he gets it

_____ 6. held under a spell

_____ 7. not able to tell the difference between colors

_____ 8. often the result of an accident

_____ 9. the money paid to workers at a given time

_____ 10. something that produces an extremely hot flame for melting things

_____ 11. to beg money from strangers on the street

_____ 12. where you can leave a baby and know he'll be safe

Review: Lessons 1·4

1   **Answer These Questions.** Choose the right answer and write it on the line.

_____   1. Where does a plumber spend most of his time working?
        (a) attic   (b) bathroom   (c) den   (d) porch

_____   2. Who would most likely wear a mask?
        (a) panhandler   (b) partner   (c) princess   (d) prowler

_____   3. Which of these jobs does not require a uniform?
        (a) baseball player   (b) nurse   (c) plumber   (d) policeman

_____   4. In which of these places would somebody be most likely to say "Shhh"?
        (a) library   (b) office   (c) showroom   (d) stadium

_____   5. Who has the most energy?
        (a) panhandler   (b) powerhouse   (c) prowler   (d) spendthrift

_____   6. If you give somebody the brushoff, you _____ him.
        (a) accept   (b) avoid   (c) flatter   (d) pressure

_____   7. If you have keen eyes, you are _____.
        (a) able to see clearly   (c) colorblind
        (b) blind   (d) in need of glasses

_____   8. On which of these animals is a yoke often used?
        (a) lions   (b) oxen   (c) roosters   (d) zebras

_____   9. Which person needs a license in order to practice?
        (a) bodyguard   (c) quarterback
        (b) president   (d) veterinarian

_____   10. Which of these fractions is the smallest amount?
        (a) $\frac{1}{2}$ (b) $\frac{1}{3}$ (c) $\frac{1}{4}$ (d) $\frac{1}{5}$

_____   11. The Nile is the longest river in _____.
        (a) Africa   (c) North America
        (b) Asia   (d) South America

_____   12. Who was the Greek god of wine?
        (a) a princess   (b) Bacchus   (c) Midas   (d) Pan

2 **Synonyms.** Match the words at the left with their synonyms.

avenue
brim
broth
doubt
earnings
equal
grubby
madam
pleasure
slack
slime
slosh

_____ 1. dirty

_____ 2. edge

_____ 3. fun

_____ 4. loose

_____ 5. mud

_____ 6. question

_____ 7. same

_____ 8. soup

_____ 9. splash

_____ 10. street

_____ 11. wages

_____ 12. woman

3 **Antonyms.** Match the words at the left with their antonyms.

brighten
brushoff
equal
fro
glum
hazy
inner
marshy
safety
strive
veteran
whisper

_____ 1. cheerful

_____ 2. clear

_____ 3. danger

_____ 4. dim

_____ 5. dry

_____ 6. give up

_____ 7. newcomer

_____ 8. outer

_____ 9. roar

_____ 10. to

_____ 11. unequal

_____ 12. welcome

4 **Common Sayings.** Do you know these sayings? Use the words at the left to fill in the blanks.

blood
broth
charm
cherries
chip
choosers
flat
glass
grain
price
shoe
sleeve
steel
stitch
stones
streak

1. A bully has "a _____ on his shoulder."

2. "A _____ in time saves nine."

3. An outlaw has "a _____ on his head."

4. "Beggars can't be _____."

5. "_____ runs thicker than water."

6. Everyone could tell from Grandpa's smile that he had "a trick up

   his _____."

7. "If the _____ fits, wear it."

8. Jimmy's bicycle was "as _____ as a pancake" after it had been hit
   by a truck.

9. "Life is just a bowl of _____."

10. "People who live in _____ houses shouldn't throw

    _____."

11. The champ had "nerves of _____."

12. The medicine worked "like a _____."

13. The poker player had "a great winning _____."

14. "Too many cooks spoil the _____."

15. You have to take everything a phony says with "a _____ of salt."

5 **Compound Words.** Choose a word from **List A** and add a word from **List B** to it to make a compound word. Study the example before you begin.

List A	List B		
√blood	blade	1.	_bloodshed_
cross	bleed	2.	_____
drop	chair	3.	_____
horse	flake		
nose	out	4.	_____
shoe	road	5.	_____
sling	√shed		
snow	shoe	6.	_____
switch	shot	7.	_____
wheel	string	8.	_____
		9.	_____
		10.	_____

List A	List B		
air	book	1.	_____
birth	bridge	2.	_____
break	craft	3.	_____
draw	down		
green	house	4.	_____
gun	lace	5.	_____
play	light		
shoe	mate	6.	_____
stop	shot	7.	_____
story	stone	8.	_____
		9.	_____
		10.	_____

6 **Helping People.** Can you figure out this quote about helping people?

A. Each of the ten sentences defines or gives a clue for a certain word. Write that word on the lines to the left of each sentence.

B. Put the letters of these words in the blanks at the bottom of the page. The quote, when all the blanks are filled in, will be a thought about helping people.

C. The first one has been done for you. Study it before you begin.

S U N D A Y
15 49 26 43 32 28

1. This is the first day of the week.

___ ___ ___ ___ ___ ___ ___
46 41 42 1 10 35 46

2. This crows so early in the morning that he is an alarm clock for farmers.

___ ___ ___ ___ ___ ___ ___ ___ ___ ___ ___ ___
46 12 44 46 6 23 12 46 39 16 29 46

3. You put milk, eggs, and other things you want to keep cold in this.

___ ___ ___ ___ ___ ___ ___
48 19 32 26 14 36 38

4. Are Earth and Mars stars or planets?

___ ___ ___ ___ ___ ___ ___ ___ ___
11 32 7 13 30 46 40 18 46 9

5. Two kinds of meat that Americans grill at picnics are hot dogs and _____.

___ ___ ___ ___ ___ ___ ___ ___
3 45 31 51 45 34 25 22

6. Detroit is located in the state of _____.

___ ___ ___ ___ ___ ___   ___ ___ ___
31 25 1 10 2 46   2 37 19

7. Grandmother makes Grandpa take this in the first story in this book.

___ ___ ___ ___ ___ ___ ___ ___
17 41 19 21 27 25 28 50

8. Thanksgiving, Christmas, and the Fourth of July are all _____.

___ ___ ___ ___ ___ ___ ___ ___ ___
48 39 22 24 39 33 27 19 12

9. This is one way that Tango got his money.

___ ___ ___ ___ ___ ___
5 8 47 20 4 46

10. When people get upset, they sometimes lose their _____.

Quote:

___ ___ ___ ___ ___ ___ ___ ___ ___   ___ ___ ___   ___ ___ S ___
 1 2 3 4 5 6 7 8 9   10 11 12   13 14 15 16

___ ___ ___ ___ ___ ___ ___   ___ ___ N ___   Y ___ ___   ___ A ___
17 18 19 20 21 22 23   24 25 26 27   28 29 30   31 32 33

___ ___ ___   ___ ___   ___   ___ ___ ___ D   ___ ___ ___ ___   ___ U ___ ___.
34 35 36   37 38   39   40 41 42 43   44 45 46 47   48 49 50 51

Word Index: Lessons 1-4

A
airtight
antonym
arise
arose
arrest
avenue

B
Bacchus
ban
bathrobe
beech
birthstone
blab
blaze
blessed
blimp
blond(e)
bloodshed
blowtorch
blubber
blueberry
blur
bonnet
bother
boyfriend
brat
breach
breadbox
brighten
brim
brittle
broth
brushoff
buttermilk

C
carefully
castor oil
chairman
champ
chant
chap
chapel
cherry
Chicago
childish
chock
chooser
chuckle
clamp
cleat
clinch
cling
clink
clog
clot
clove

clover
clump
coffeepot
colorblind
contest
cotton
craft
cram
crank
creak
creaky
crest
cripple
crossbar
crossroad
cruel
cuss
custard

D
daze
deathly
decoy
disobey
doubt
drawbridge
dropout

E
earnings
enlarge
equal
equally
eyebrow

F
first-rate
flabby
flatter
flattery
flex
flick
floss
flown
flung
follow
follower
fraction
Fred
fret
fringe
fro
frost
frostbite
frosting
fuzz

G
galoshes
gap

gape
ghost
glassful
glaze
Glen
glider
glittery
glob
glum
granddaughter
grandpa
grandson
grandstand
grasp
grant
grate
grateful
Greenland
grim
grope
grubby
gunshot

H
half-wit
haste
haze
hazy
headline
he's
hitch
horseshoe
host
humid
humor
humorous
hutch

I
inner
insurance
intelligent
interest

J
jig
jiggle
Jimmy
joyfully

K
keen

L
license
lightheaded
lion

M
madam
madhouse
mane
Mars
marsh
marshmallow
marshy
meantime
Midas
mixed
moneybags
mouthpiece
mustard
mutt

N
Nile
nosebleed

O
obey
odds
opening
outburst
outlaw
overpaid

P
palace
Pan
panhandle
panhandler
Paris
partner
payroll
pencil
petal
placement
plainclothes
planter
playmate
playpen
pleasure
pliers
plop
pluck
plumber
potpie
power
powerhouse
prank
pressure
prime
princess
prod
prowl
prowler

Q
quiz

R
ranch
rap
reaction
reorder
rind
roost
rooster
ruby

S
safety
salute
sh!
shabby
shall
shed
shipshape
shiver
shoe
shoelace
shoestring
shortchange
showroom
shudder
slack
slash
slate
slime
slimy
slingshot
slit
slope
slosh
slug
slur
snitch
snowflake
somewhere
solo
spellbound
stab
stack
stag
stagger
steady
steeple
stench
stiff
stole
stoplight
storybook
strangle
strangler

strengthen
strep
stretcher
stride
strive
strut
stub
Susan
switchblade
synonym

T
tango
taxi
they'd
torch
train wreck

U
unequal
uniform
unlighted

V
vast
vent
vet
veteran
veterinarian

W
weakness
welcome
wept
wheelchair
whiplash
whisper
whistle
wick
wishbone
wishy-washy
wit

X

Y
yeast
yoke

Z
zebra

Lesson 5

Review of Consonant Blends: Part 4

dr:	draft	dredge	drifter	drive-in	droop	drunken
tr:	tract	trade-in	treaty	trench	trespass	troublesome
th:	thatched	theme	thigh	thorough	thoroughly	thickness
	theirs	they'll	thee	thou	thereabout	thereafter
	bathmat	footpath	moth	mothball	tollbooth	withdraw
thr:	thrash	thresh	thresher	thriller	throttle	throwaway
tw:	twang	tweed	tweezers	twentieth	twig	twitch

1 **Word Meanings.** Use the words at the left to fill in the blanks.

drifter
droop
mothballs
thigh
thorough
thou
thriller
throttle
tollbooth
trade-in
treaty
trench
trespass
tweezers
twitch

_____ 1. a booth where a toll is paid by a driver

_____ 2. a ditch

_____ 3. a person who moves from place to place or job to job

_____ 4. a really exciting story or movie

_____ 5. a tool used for plucking eyebrows

_____ 6. an agreement between two or more states or countries containing terms of peace, trade, etc.

_____ 7. another word for *you*

_____ 8. fully done

_____ 9. something people store their clothing in to keep moths from eating them

_____ 10. something accepted as part of a payment for buying something new

_____ 11. the part of the body between the hip and the knee

_____ 12. to bend or hang down

_____ 13. to invade the property of another person without his consent

_____ 14. to move suddenly; to jerk

_____ 15. to strangle or choke

brooded	necklace	stock	patience
silver	unlocked	value	eager
Denver	receipt	opportunity	author

The Oldest Trick in the World: Part I

George, without looking, could feel his boss watching every move he made. How long, he brooded, had he worked for Mr. Green? Four years? And before that, he had worked at the Court Jewelry Store for six years. He knew everything there was to know about gems, gold and silver, and yet Mr. Green continued to treat him as if he were a beginner.

"George."

"Sir?"

"I've decided to go to that meeting in Denver. That means I won't be in until Friday. I'll be leaving the store in your hands."

George cheered up. "I can handle it, Mr. Green. You go ahead and have a good time in Denver. Miss Barns and I will look after everything here."

Mr. Green left on the evening flight and early the next morning, soon after George and Miss Barns opened the store, the cowboy came in.

"May I help you?" George asked.

"I'd like to see something in a diamond necklace," said the cowboy.

"Certainly. Did you have anything in mind? A certain price range perhaps?"

"Hadn't really thought about it. Let's see what you have."

George brought out several necklaces. On each was a small price tag, the price written on it in ink. The cowboy glanced at them. "Five hundred dollars," he said. "Are these the best you have?"

"Oh, no—we have some here," George pointed to the glass case at his back, "which run as high as forty-five hundred dollars."

"Well, haul them out, son," the man said in a friendly tone. As George unlocked the case, he added, "What's your name?"

"George, sir."

"Well, George, what's the going price on that one?"

"That's," George turned the price tag, "$3,899.99, sir."

"Fine," the cowboy grinned, "I'll take it. You'll take a check?" He drew a leather checkbook from his pocket and opened it on the counter. The cowboy cheerfully began to fill in the check. "George, I want you to take this check to my bank and cash it. I'm leaving town this afternoon on business, but I'll be back on Friday to pick up the necklace. Okay?"

"Why, okay." George breathed, relaxing. He added the cost, including tax, completed the receipt, and the cowboy handed him the check.

"Now I'd like to see your finest diamond ring."

"Of course," George looked at the check, "Mr. James. May I ask the price range?"

"Oh, somewhere around twenty thousand. Let's start there."

"I'm afraid we don't keep a display of diamonds in that price range, sir. Eight thousand would be our best in stock."

The cowboy cocked his head and made a clicking noise with his tongue. George gazed at him for a moment, his mind working fast. Then, all at once, he nodded and smiled as if he had made a great discovery. He said, "You know, I can have a display of higher-priced rings here when you come in to pick up the necklace."

"Why, that sounds like a fine idea, George."

"Leave it to me, sir," said George, his voice smooth. "I know exactly what you want."

"See you Friday, then," said the cowboy.

Later in the day George went to the bank printed on Mr. James's check. He expected no trouble cashing the check and had none.

The next morning he met with the manager of the main branch of the jewelry store. They chose a display of rings at a total value of $247,000. The rings were placed in a black leather case which was then handcuffed to George's left wrist. The store guard went with him across town in a cab.

The next day, George phoned in sick.

"You just stay home in bed," said Miss Barns in a gentle and concerned tone. "I'll look after things here."

George hung up the phone and smiled. Miss Barns was treating him with more respect since what he had come to think of as the James opportunity. It was truly strange, he thought, how such a small thing could change a man's life. All you had to do was wait. It was just a matter of patience.

Continued in the next lesson . . .

2 **About the Story.** Answer these questions.

1. True or false? If the statement is true, write *true* on the line to the left. If the statement is false, write *false* AND rewrite the sentence so it is a true statement. Study the example before you begin.

false   a. George was a beginner in the jewelry business.

    George had worked in the jewelry business for at least ten years.

_____ b. Mr. Green is very pleased with George's work.

_____

_____ c. Both Mr. Green and Mr. James will be returning to the jewelry store on Friday.

_____

_____ d. Mr. James seems more eager to spend his money on a ring than on a necklace.

_____

_____ e. George thinks he will have no problem cashing Mr. James's check.

_____

_____ f. Miss Barns is impressed with George's handling of Mr. James.

_____

_____ g. George goes to the main branch to see if he can work there.

_____

_____ h. George calls in sick because he is sick.

_____

_____ i. At the end of this part of the story, George is afraid.

_____

_____ j. This story takes place in Denver.

_____

2. Pretend that you are the author of this story. How would you end it?

_____

_____

3 **Working with Consonant Blends and Digraphs.** Put the consonant blends above each sentence in the right place so the sentences make sense. Study the example before you begin.

1. **br   cl   cr   dr   ~~fl~~   fr   sh   st   tr**

_Fl_icking his cigarette into the bu__es, the __ifter __ood at the __ossroad, __ying

to decide which route would __ing him __oser to the __eeway.

2. **br   cl   fr   gl   pl   pr   st   th   wh**

"__y," he __ooded out loud as he __anced at the dark __ouds above, "did I ever

__ink I would find more __easure in the __eedom of the open road than in

__aying home and holding down a __oper job."

3. **dr   dr   dr   fr   sh   st   st   th   tr**

Then, a pickup __uck pulled up alongside the __ifter, and the __iver __uck his

head out the window and __outed in a __iendly voice, "Hey, you gonna __and

__ere __eaming all day, or do you want a lift?"

4. **ch   dr   dr   sh   sh   st   th   th   tr**

As __ey __ove along, the __iver said, "I sure wi__ I could ju__ __uck

everything and head nor__ for some hunting and __out fi__ing."

5. **br   dr   gr   gr   pl   pr   st   th   tr**

"Well," said the __ifter, "I guess that ju__ goes to __ove the __ass always seems

__eener on the other side of the __acks 'cause I'm so __oke and hungry right now

that I'm __inking there's no __ace like home."

4 **Which Word Does Not Fit?** Choose the word in each line that does not fit with the rest.

1. pin   silver   bracelet   earrings   necklace   _____

2. cane   limp   crutches   stretcher   wheelchair   _____

3. elm   ivy   oak   beech   chestnut   _____

4. nails   hammer   pliers   wrench   screwdriver   _____

5. boots   galoshes   slippers   sneakers   stockings   _____

6. basin   towel   bathmat   dentist   toothbrush   _____

7. hip   toe   thigh   spleen   knee   _____

8. Ohio   Texas   Denver   California New Hampshire _____

9. silk   tweed   cotton   leather   tailor   _____

10. fee   tax   toll   charge   receipt   _____

5 **Breaking Words into Syllables.** Rewrite each word listed below, in syllables, on the lines to the right. The number after each word tells you how many syllables are in that word. Study the example before you begin.

1. arrest (2)   _ar·rest_____   9. trespass (2)   _____

2. brittle (2)   _____   10. receipt (2)   _____

3. frostbite (2) _____   11. jiggle (2)   _____

4. unlock (2)   _____   12. pencil (2)   _____

5. partner (2)   _____   13. joyfully (3)   _____

6. withdraw (2) _____   14. carefully (3) _____

7. silver (2)   _____   15. intelligent (4) _____

8. shameful (2) _____   16. thereabout (3) _____

6 **Where Can You Find It?** Match each word at the left with the place in which you can find it.

bloodshed
busybody
buttermilk
castor oil
Chicago
Egypt
footpath
grandstand
Paris
princess
sneakers
stench
stoplight
tollbooth
wheelchair

_____ 1. battle

_____ 2. forest

_____ 3. France

_____ 4. hospital

_____ 5. in others' business

_____ 6. locker

_____ 7. medicine chest

_____ 8. northeastern Africa

_____ 9. palace

_____ 10. refrigerator

_____ 11. stadium

_____ 12. street

_____ 13. the Midwest

_____ 14. trash can

_____ 15. turnpike

Lesson 6

Review of Consonant Blends: Part 5

sk:	sketchbook	sketchy	skillet	skim	skimp	skit
sc:	scab	scalp	scarce	scarcely	Scotland	scum
scr:	scrapbook	scramble	scrawl	screwball	scribble	Scripture
sm:	smallpox	smelly	smirk	smock	smother	smuggle
sn:	snack bar	snare	snazzy	snipe	snowy	snuff
sw:	swank	sway	swelling	swimsuit	swore	swollen

1 **Word Meanings.** Use the words at the left to fill in the blanks.

scab
scarcely
Scotland
scrawl
screwball
scribble
skillet
skimp
skit
smock
smother
smuggle
snare
swimsuit
swank

_____ 1. a country located north of England

_____ 2. a loose piece of clothing worn to protect a person's good clothes while he's working

_____ 3. a short, funny act performed in front of a group of people

_____ 4. a slang word used to describe something really fancy

_____ 5. barely; hardly

_____ 6. something people wear in the ocean, lake, pool, etc.

_____ 7. the covering on a wound that is getting better

_____ 8. something used to fry scrambled eggs, bacon, pork chops, etc.

_____ 9. a certain kind of baseball pitch; also a slang term for a nutty person

_____ 10. to do something too fast or carelessly; to be very thrifty with money

_____ 11. to import or export goods without paying the lawful charges or fees

_____ 12. to keep from breathing; to hide or conceal

_____ 13. to trap someone or something

_____ 14. to write so fast that you can hardly read what's been written

_____ 15. another word for Answer 14

Words for Study

splendid	velvet	jewel	replacement
loafers	necessary	sprang	investment
impatience	unsteady	drawstring	Los Angeles

The Oldest Trick in the World: Part II

Mr. Green returned from Denver Thursday evening, and on Friday morning he was already in the store talking to Miss Barns when George came in to work. As George entered, Mr. Green spun around and marched over to shake his hand.

"Good work, George," he said. "Miss Barns told me all about it." He laughed and slapped George on the shoulder.

"Thank you, sir," George said without smiling.

"When did this Mr. James say he'd be here?"

"First thing in the morning."

"Splendid! Now when he comes in, I'll take it from there."

As he spoke, the cowboy walked through the door dressed in brown loafers, a suit and necktie, and a light overcoat.

"How are you, George?" he said as though greeting an old friend.

"Fine, sir," George replied in a dull voice.

Mr. Green rushed over and stretched his hand across the counter. "Mr. James? I'm Mr. Green, the manager. I understand George here has been very helpful to you."

"Yes, sir, he has been that. I'm extremely pleased."

"Good, good. George, would you get Mr. James's necklace from the safe? And the rings?" He turned to the cowboy. "Do you still wish to buy the ring?"

"Yes, of course," James replied with impatience.

"George," Mr. Green called, "hurry it a little please."

George returned with a velvet box in one hand and a velvet display board of gleaming rings in the other. He laid them gently on the counter.

"If you'd like to see the necklace . . ." said Mr. Green.

"That won't be necessary," the cowboy replied. "Miss! The alarm," he said, "is three feet to your left. George, don't move a muscle toward it. I like you. Don't make me do anything foolish. You, Miss, lock that door."

With a very unsteady walk, Miss Barns went to the front door and locked it.

"Into the back room," the cowboy said. "You too, Miss. Let's go."

Two hours later, the police were talking to Mr. Green, Miss Barns, and George. White tape that Mr. James had used to tie them up with lay everywhere. One of the officers closed his notebook.

"Well, it's just too bad you people took so long to reach the alarm. Two hours is a long start. When this trick is used in a jewel robbery, it gives the thief too much time."

"Trick? Did you say trick, officer?" Mr. Green, who had been sitting in a slouched way holding his head, sprang up. "What do you mean, trick?"

"It's the oldest trick in the world," said the officer flatly. "The thief has everything set up so that what he wants is ready and waiting for him. No searching, no broken glass, no noise, no waiting—quick and easy. He has, in effect, placed an order for the robbery." He grinned. "Like a shopping list. You know?"

"Do you hear that, George? The world's oldest trick! You fool!" he screamed. "You're fired, George! Get out of here. Get out of my sight."

The officer looked at them with tired eyes. "There will be statements to sign or mug shots to go over," he said and turned to leave. "Just don't anyone leave town."

Alone in his apartment, George put a fresh pot of coffee on the stove. While it was perking, he took the small black bag from the pocket of his coat, spread the drawstring, and poured the fourteen rings on the table.

He smiled. One day off work, he thought, had been plenty of time to buy phony replacements around town. Although they had cost him a little more than he had expected, it was still a fine investment.

The oldest trick in the world, he mused, and laughed out loud. Well, of course it was. He would have been an utter fool not to have seen it ten minutes after talking to James, just as he had seen it at the Court Jewelry Store in Boston six years ago.

In a few months he would leave the city and find a new job in another jewelry store. Los Angeles, perhaps. Yes, he had always liked the idea of living in California. Then he would just wait. There would always be another cowboy along. It was just a matter of patience.

Adapted with permission of Michael Stephenson. Copyright © 1980 by Davis Publications, Inc.; first published in *Alfred Hitchcock's Mystery Magazine.*

2 **About the Story.** Answer these questions.

1. Mr. Green reacts in three different ways to George in this part of the story. Put these reactions in the order in which they happen. After each reaction, write the reason that Mr. Green responds to George in this way.

> He fires George.
> He orders George about.
> He shakes George's hand.

How Mr. Green Reacts	**Reason**
a. _____	_____
b. _____	_____
c. _____	_____

2. Describe "the oldest trick in the world."

_____

_____

_____

3. Now that you have read the end of the story, explain why George had called in sick in Part I.

_____

4. How do you know that Mr. Green was completely wrong in having regarded George as a beginner in the jewelry business?

_____

_____

5. What is the plan that George decides upon as he is fixing himself a cup of coffee in his apartment at the end of the story?

_____

_____

6. Do you hope that George gets away with what he has done, or do you want him to get caught? Be sure to explain the reason for your answer.

_____

_____

3 **More Work with Consonant Blends and Digraphs.** Put the consonant blends above each sentence in the right place so the sentences make sense. Study the example before you begin.

1. **ch   ch   cr   gr   pl   scr   sn   ~~st~~   st**

   There was an outbur _st_ of ___eers when the ___ack bar at the bea___ opened, and a

   hun___y ___owd ___ambled for fir___ ___ace in line.

2. **ch   ch   dr   fr   fr   gr   pr   sh   st**

   The ___ices were not ___eap, but the ___ocolate milk ___akes and ___ench ___ies

   were so ___eat that people ___ove for miles ju___ to buy them.

3. **cr   dr   fl   gl   gl   st   st   st**

   ___anding behind the ___owded counter, the ___oomy manager ___ung his cigarette

   ___ub into the ___ain and ___ared at all the cu___omers.

4. **dr   sh   sh   st   sn   sw   sw   th**

   The sight of all ___ese people ___essed in ___orts, ___eakers, ___imsuits and ___eat

   ___irts disgu___ed him.

5. **ch   cr   gr   pl   scr   sh   st   sw   th**

   As he watched somebody old enough to be his ___andfather ___ove a ___eaming

   ___ild out of his ___ace in the line, the manager ___ore ___at if he didn't find himself

   another job by Augu___, he would surely go ___azy.

4 Antonyms. Match the words at the left with their antonyms.

clumsy
grouchy
import
joyful
melted
plural
restrain
scarce
shabby
skinny
southwestern
strengthen
thorough
thrifty
unnecessary

_____ 1. careless

_____ 2. common

_____ 3. export

_____ 4. frozen

_____ 5. graceful

_____ 6. grim

_____ 7. necessary

_____ 8. northeastern

_____ 9. overweight

_____ 10. pleasant

_____ 11. release

_____ 12. singular

_____ 13. snazzy

_____ 14. wasteful

_____ 15. weaken

5 **Words Beginning with *re-*.** Use the words at the left to fill in the blanks so the sentences make sense.

receipt
recording
refunded
refused
regarded
rejected
repeated
replace
replied
respect
restrain
retreat

1. When Mrs. Smith discovered that the toaster she had just bought didn't work properly, she tried to get her money _____.

2. The clerk at the hardware store said that he couldn't give her any money unless she had a _____ to prove she had bought the toaster in their store.

3. Mrs. Smith _____, "But I threw it away!"

4. The clerk just shrugged his shoulders and _____ the store's rule about returning things.

5. "Can't you at least _____ the toaster with one that works properly?" Mrs. Smith cried.

6. The clerk _____ to answer her question.

7. "With all due _____," Mrs. Smith declared, "you are the rudest clerk I've ever met."

8. The clerk was busy _____ numbers in a brown notebook and pretended that he hadn't even heard her.

9. Mrs. Smith felt totally _____ and began to cry her heart out right in the middle of the store.

10. The clerk _____ her with cold eyes and said in an icy voice, "Madam, your tears are smudging my numbers."

11. It was all Mrs. Smith could do to _____ herself from smashing this stupid clerk with her handbag.

12. Instead, she ripped a handful of pages from the clerk's notebook and beat a fast _____ to her car.

Lesson 7

Review of Consonant Blends: Part 6

sp:	spareribs	spearmint	speedway	spike	spotted	spur
spl:	splashdown	splashy	splatter	splendidly	splotch	splutter
spr:	sprig	springtime	sprinkle	spruce	sprung	
shr:	shriek	shrine	shrivel	shrunken	shrubbery	
squ:	squad	squawk	squash	squeamish	squid	
wh:	whereabouts	whirlpool	White House	whop	whopper	
sch:	schooner	schoolhouse	schoolroom	schoolteacher		
chr:	Christ-like	Chris	Christopher	christen		

1 Word Meanings. Use the words at the left to fill in the blanks.

shriek
shrubbery
spareribs
spearmint
speedway
splatter
splotch
spurs
squad
squash
squawk
squeamish
squid
White House
whop
whopper

_____ 1. a course for automobile racing

_____ 2. pork ribs with most of the meat trimmed off

_____ 3. a game played in a walled court with a racket and a hard rubber ball; also the name of a plant

_____ 4. a group of shrubs

_____ 5. a long thin sea animal with ten arms that is often used for fish bait

_____ 6. a shrill outcry; screech

_____ 7. a small group of people brought together for a certain job or task

_____ 8. a stain or spot

_____ 9. anything that is really huge; a huge lie

_____ 10. what cowboys wear on their boots to move their horses forward

_____ 11. a kind of chewing gum

_____ 12. where the President of the United States lives

_____ 13. a word describing a person who gets upset by such things as the sight of blood

_____ 14. to complain

_____ 15. to hit, strike or beat someone

_____ 16. to splash with liquid

Words for Study

regret	discussion	reward	we've
envelope	glory	company	self-pity
invitation	post	loan shark	evil

The Necklace

Mrs. Carpenter was a pretty and charming woman who was married to a clerk. She was an extremely unhappy woman, for she longed for beautiful evening clothes and jewelry. Those were the things she wanted; she felt that was the kind of life for her. However, she could not afford fine clothes and jewelry, so she would weep for days on end from regret and anger.

Then one evening, her husband came home proudly holding out a large envelope. "Look," he said, "I've got something for you."

The printed card was an invitation to a party on Friday, January 18. Instead of being delighted as her husband had hoped, she tossed the invitation on the table in an angry manner. "What good is that to me?" she replied. "I don't have an evening dress and therefore I can't go. Give the card to some friend at the office whose wife can dress better than I can."

After much discussion, Mr. Carpenter agreed to give her the money he had been saving for a new gun so that she could buy a dress. As the day of the party grew near, Mrs. Carpenter was still sad and moody. It seemed that she was upset because she didn't own a single piece of jewelry to wear with her new dress.

But her husband exclaimed, "My, but you're silly! Go see your friend Mrs. Dennis and ask her to lend you some jewelry."

She gave a cry of joy, "Why, that's so! I hadn't thought of that."

The next day she paid her friend a visit and told her of her problem. Mrs. Dennis brought over a large jewel box and said, "Pick something out, my dear."

Mrs. Carpenter found a splendid diamond necklace, and her pulse beat faster with longing. "Could I borrow just that—just that and nothing else?"

"Why, of course."

The day of the party arrived. Mrs. Carpenter was the prettiest one there. All the men turned to look at her and begged to meet her. She danced madly, wildly, drunk with happiness. They left around four o'clock in the morning. Her husband, since midnight, had been dozing in a small, empty sitting room.

When they got home, Mrs. Carpenter stood before the mirror to see herself once again in all her glory. Suddenly, she gave a cry. The necklace was gone. Mr. and Mrs. Carpenter hunted everywhere, through the folds of the dress, through the folds of the coat, in the pockets. They found nothing.

Mr. Carpenter went to the police, to the newspapers to post a reward, to the cab company, everywhere the slightest hope drove him. At the end of the week, they had given up all hope.

"We'll have to write your friend," Mr. Carpenter said, "to tell her you have broken the catch and are having it repaired."

The next day they took the case to the jewelry store whose name they found inside. "I didn't sell that necklace, sir," the man behind the counter said. "I only gave the case."

They found, in a shop on Third Street, a string of diamonds which seemed exactly like the one they were seeking. It was priced at $40,000. They could get it for $36,000.

Mr. Carpenter had $18,000 in the bank. He would borrow the rest. He signed notes, made bad deals, did business with loan sharks.

Each month notes had to be paid, and others renewed to give more time. Mrs. Carpenter began to learn about the terrible life that the poor live. Her husband worked nights. And this kind of life went on for ten years.

At last, all was paid back. Mrs. Carpenter looked like an old woman now. She was heavy, rough, and harsh. Her hair was stringy, her clothing was shabby, her hands were red, and her voice was shrill.

Then one Sunday when she had gone for a walk, she suddenly saw Mrs. Dennis, who still looked young, beautiful, and charming.

Mrs. Carpenter felt a rush of feelings. Should she speak to her? Of course. And now that everything was paid off, she would tell her the whole story. Why not?

She went toward her. "Hello, Martha."

The other, not even knowing who she was, showed surprise at being spoken to by this common woman.

"It's me, Martha. I'm Anne Carpenter."

Her friend gave a cry. "Oh, my poor Anne, how you've changed!"

"Yes, I've had a hard time since last seeing you—and all because of you. Do you remember that diamond necklace you loaned me?"

"Yes, but what about it?"

"Well, I lost it. I bought you another just like it. And we've been paying for it for ten years. It's over now, and I'm glad of it."

Mrs. Dennis stopped short. "You mean to say you bought a diamond necklace to replace mine?"

"Yes."

Mrs. Dennis, quite overcome with feeling, took her by the hands. "Oh, my poor Anne. But mine wasn't real. Why, at most it was worth only five hundred dollars!"

2 About the Story. Put the letter of the answer on the line to the left.

_____ 1. Mr. Carpenter is a _____.

    (a) clerk   (c) loan shark

    (b) jeweler   (d) postman

_____ 2. When Mrs. Carpenter sees the invitation to the party, she feels like _____.

    (a) buying some jewelry   (c) crying

    (b) calling Mrs. Dennis   (d) flattering her husband

_____ 3. At the party, Mrs. Carpenter _____.

    (a) dances happily until midnight

    (b) worries that she hasn't worn enough jewelry

    (c) tells her husband how grateful she feels

    (d) feels more excited about life than she has for a long time

_____ 4. Mr. Carpenter had wanted to go to the party because _____.

    (a) he really enjoys dancing

    (b) he thinks his wife will really enjoy it

    (c) he wants to impress his boss

    (d) he wants to show off his beautiful wife to his friends

_____ 5. Mr. Carpenter does all of these things to pay for the necklace except _____.

    (a) borrow money   (c) sell his gun

    (b) make deals with loan sharks   (d) work an extra job

_____ 6. Mrs. Dennis doesn't speak to Mrs. Carpenter at first when the two women meet because _____.

    (a) she does not know who this woman is

    (b) she does not remember Mrs. Carpenter's name

    (c) she is a snob

    (d) she is angry with her

_____ 7. When Mrs. Dennis hears Mrs. Carpenter's story, she _____.

    (a) gives Mrs. Carpenter the brushoff

    (b) is filled with pity for her friend

    (c) is filled with self-pity

    (d) is happy to learn that she now owns a real diamond necklace

_____ 8. All of these are hints given by the author that the necklace is fake except _____.

    (a) Mr. and Mrs. Carpenter can't find the necklace

    (b) Mrs. Dennis doesn't mind at all if Mrs. Carpenter borrows the necklace

    (c) Mrs. Dennis doesn't pressure Mrs. Carpenter to return the necklace promptly

    (d) the jeweler had sold only the case to Mrs. Dennis

_____ 9. The word that best describes Mrs. Carpenter is _____.

    (a) hardworking   (c) self pitying

    (b) kindhearted   (d) well-to-do

_____ 10. Which of these sayings describes a lesson that we can all learn from this story?

    (a) A watched pot never boils.   (c) Don't count your chickens until they're hatched.

    (b) Money is the root of all evil.   (d) All that glitters is not gold.

3 **If You Were the Author.** If the story had continued for a few more sentences, how do you think Mrs. Carpenter would have reacted when she learned that the necklace she borrowed was not real?

_____

_____

_____

_____

4 **Consonants and Consonant Blends.** Use the words at the left to fill in the blanks.

cramp
ramp
stamp
tramp

1. The _____ had such a _____ in his left leg that he wasn't even

able to _____ out the fire he had made just a few yards from

the _____.

flatter
platter
shattered
splattering

2. Aunt Ann was just about to _____ Uncle Dan for being such a fine

host when he tripped over the carpet and dropped the _____ of fried

chicken which _____ on the floor, _____ grease all over
the place.

dare
glare
scared

3. Ms. Smith was so _____ of her neighbor who always seemed to _____

at everybody that she didn't _____ refuse his invitation.

clenched
drenched
stench
trenches

4. _____ from the sudden downpour, the commander _____

his fists and prayed that his men in the _____ would be able to bear

the _____ of the many nearby corpses.

hitch
snitched
switch
twitch
witch

5. As he watched his dad _____ up his pants before picking up

the _____, Glen's jaw began to _____, and he just knew that

the old _____ who lived next door had _____ on him.

crop
flop
plopping
shop
stop

6. Because Ruby's first day at the _____ had been a complete _____ and, at home, the insects had destroyed her entire tomato _____, no one even tried to _____ her from _____ down on the couch and having a good cry.

block
clock
flocked
shocked
smock

7. Wiping her hands on her _____, Susan glanced at the _____ and was _____ to notice that the children on the _____ who normally _____ into her kitchen for snacks after school were late.

chore
shore
swore

8. Steve thought that driving to the _____ on a humid August weekend was such a _____ that he _____ he'd never do it again.

drummed
glum
humming
scum

9. Cinderella tried to pull herself out of her _____ mood by _____ a tune as she _____ her fingers on the basin and wondered how she would ever remove the _____.

blushed
brushing
crush
slush

10. Anne, _____ the _____ from the window of her father's van, _____ as the boy she had a _____ on drove by.

5 **Breaking Words into Syllables.** Rewrite each word listed below, in syllables, on the lines to the right. The number after each word tells you how many syllables are in that word.

1. investment (3) _____

2. flatly (2) _____

3. splendid (2) _____

4. restrain (2) _____

5. necessary (4) _____

6. marshmallow (3) _____

7. carelessly (3) _____

8. turnpike (2) _____

9. velvet (2) _____

10. replacement (3) _____

11. thickness (2) _____

12. drawstring (2) _____

13. export (2) _____

14. alongside (3) _____

15. blubber (2) _____

16. opportunity (5) _____

6   **More Words Beginning with re-.** Use the words at the left to fill in the blanks.

reborn
recite
recline
reflect
reform
regret
reveal
reverse
review
revolve
revolver
reward

_____ 1. a gun that can be fired quickly without reloading

_____ 2. having new life

_____ 3. money given for the return of something lost

_____ 4. to feel sorry about something that has been done

_____ 5. to go over a lesson or subject again

_____ 6. to lie down or lean back

_____ 7. to make better by removing faults

_____ 8. to move in a circle around a point

_____ 9. to show or display; to make known something that's been hidden

_____ 10. to speak out loud or to tell something in detail

_____ 11. to think about something

_____ 12. to turn backward

Lesson 8

Review of Vowel Combinations: Part 1

ai:	saint	lain	vain	traitor	hailstorm
au:	fraud	applaud	applause	clause	taut
ēa:	ease	easygoing	heal	peak	
ĕa:	headway	cleanse	cleanser	treasure	
ee:	creek	creed	reed	feedback	
oa:	goat	toad	croak	boastful	
oi:	loin	groin	toilet	poise	
oo:	loop	loophole	boost	groove	
ou:	mount	fountain	hound	greyhound	
ue:	cue	barbecue	argue	issue	

1   **Word Meanings.** Use the words at the left to fill in the blanks.

barbecue
cleanse
creed
creek
cue
easygoing
fraud
hound
loophole
taut
traitor
vain

_____ 1. a dog with drooping ears, a short coat and a deep voice that is used for hunting

_____ 2. a grill, pit, or outdoor fireplace for roasting meat

_____ 3. a hint or reminder; in the game of pool, the long rod used to move the ball forward

_____ 4. a trick practiced in order to gain something that is not lawful or fair

_____ 5. a person who commits a crime against his country

_____ 6. a small stream; a brook

_____ 7. a statement of beliefs

_____ 8. a way of getting out of a troublesome spot—for example, a contract or law worded in such a way that a person can break it

_____ 9. living without intense concern; peaceful

_____ 10. pulled or drawn tight; tense; strained

_____ 11. to free from dirt or guilt

_____ 12. showing too much pride; boastful

Words for Study

tinkle	overjoyed	youth	suggestion
yours	wrestle	poisoner	members
master	druggist	suggests	gasped

Eight Baskets of Gold

There was once a gang of young men who spent their days and nights drinking and dancing and carrying on. Early one morning as three of the young men sat in a bar waiting for a drink, they heard a bell tinkle as a corpse was being carried to the grave. One of them ordered a boy to find out whose corpse was passing by.

"Sir," said the boy, "there is no need to ask. I know him and so do you. He used to be a friend of yours. But last night when he was there on the bench, dead drunk, he was suddenly killed. That sneak thief that men call Death speared his heart in two and went away without saying a word. So, master, wherever you go, be on your guard. Be ready to meet him from now on."

The three young men only laughed at him. They boasted that they'd go out at once and kill the false traitor, Death.

They hadn't gone half a mile before they met a poor old man who told them that if they kept going for a short while, they would find Death waiting for them under an oak tree.

They ran as fast as they could go to the oak tree. There, they found a pile of golden coins on the ground—eight baskets of them. They were so overjoyed by this sight that they gave up the idea of seeking Death.

The most evil of the three young men spoke first: "Lady Luck has given us this treasure so that we may spend the rest of our lives having a good time. We must be careful and carry these baskets off by night. So let's draw lots to see who shall run to town as fast as he can and bring us bread and wine. The other two of us shall remain here to keep watch over the treasure. When night comes, we'll carry it wherever we think best."

So lots were drawn to see where the luck would fall. It fell on the youngest, who set off at once for town. As soon as he was gone, one of the two said to his friend, "Our friend has gone, and here's a pile of gold that's to be split up among three of us. Nevertheless, wouldn't it be a fine thing if I can fix things so that it would be split between us two alone?"

The other answered, "I don't see how we can get away with it. He knows that the gold is here with us. What will we do?"

"I can tell you exactly what to do. When he returns, pretend that you want to wrestle with him just for fun. While you're wrestling, I'll stab him. Then all this gold will be ours, and we can spend the rest of our lives having a good time."

Thus these two men agreed to kill the third.

In the meantime, as the youngest ran toward the town, he could think only about the coins. "Oh, Lord," he said, "how I'd like the treasure all to myself! No man under the throne of God would live as well as I could!"

And so the youngest man ran on into town, straight to a druggist and asked him for poison to kill rats.

"You shall have it," the druggist said. "And I swear to you that this poison is so bad that it will kill anything in the world that eats as little as a grain of it. He'll die in a shorter time than it takes you to walk a mile."

So this young man bought a box of this poison and ran with it to a man in the next street from whom he borrowed three large bottles. He poured the poison into two of them, but kept the third one clean for his own drink—because, you see, he planned to work all night carrying the gold out of the place by the oak tree. And when this evil youth had filled his three big bottles with wine, he returned to his friends.

Just as they had planned, the two friends jumped on him and killed him. And when this was done, the first one said, "Now let's sit down and have a drink to celebrate. We can hide his body later." With that he reached for a bottle—and by chance picked up one that had poison in it. He drank and offered some to his friend. Just as the druggist had said, they were dead in the time it would take a man to walk a mile.

Thus ended these two murderers and the false poisoner, too.

2 **About the Story.** Answer these questions.

1. Is it really Lady Luck who gives the three young men the treasure? If your answer is *no*, then who does put the gold under the tree? _____

2. Why do you think one of the young men suggests that they wait until dark to carry away the treasure? _____

   _____

3. What suggestion does one of the two men who remains with the gold make to the other?

   _____

   _____

4. Meanwhile, what scheme does the youngest man have in mind?

   _____

5. If the two men had drunk from the bottle that had no poison, what do you think would have happened next in the story?

   _____

   _____

6. Do you think these men deserve what happened to them? Be sure to explain your answer.

   _____

   _____

3 **Review of Vowel Sounds.** Use the words at the left to fill in the blanks.

creek
croak
crook

1. While the _____ was hiding out by the _____, he heard something _____ behind him.

hand
hind
hound

2. The _____ stood on his _____ legs and licked the owner's _____.

beast
boasted
boost

3. The cowboy _____ that he could _____ the _____ into the truck without any help from his partner.

hailstorm
heal
heel

4. The wound that Fred got on his _____ while running from his car to the house during the _____ took a long time to _____.

grain
groaned
groin

5. Even though Bud _____ in pain when he pulled his _____ muscle, he refused to quit because he didn't have one _____ of common sense.

peas
poise
pose

6. While eating dinner, Tim was so tense about asking Kate to marry him that he completely lost his _____ and spilled the bowl of _____ all over the table before he could even _____ the question.

4 **Where Would You Find This?** Choose the word in the row that tells you where you would most likely find the first word and circle it. Study the example before you begin.

1. **Los Angeles:** (California) Ohio Michigan Washington
2. **applause:** chapel concert galley library
3. **fountain:** forest park schoolroom thruway
4. **squid:** fishbowl North Pole ocean pond
5. **marshmallow:** chocolate cocoa gingerbread soda
6. **Frenchman:** Amsterdam Huron Paris Pearl Harbor
7. **wishbone:** chicken lamb roast beef veal
8. **grate:** bedroom birdhouse fireplace harbor
9. **uniform:** Christian policeman southpaw teller
10. **White House:** Baltimore Chicago Los Angeles Washington, D.C.

5   **Words Beginning with *pre-*.** Use the words at the left to fill in the blanks.

precise
predicted
prepare
prescribed
present
pretended
prevent
preview

1. The cook could not remember the _____ time that she discovered the corpse in the cellar.

2. She told the officers that she had just started to _____ dinner when she heard a strange noise coming from the cellar.

3. She was so scared that she _____ she hadn't heard anything and continued to peel the potatoes for the beef stew.

4. When asked what the other members of the household had been doing at the time,

   she replied that they had been discussing a _____ of a movie they wanted to see.

5. Mrs. Charles had fainted when she learned of the corpse, and the doctor

   _____ complete rest.

6. Mr. Charles tried to _____ reporters from entering the house, but he was not successful.

7. When Mr. Charles began to _____ his side of the story, one of the officers switched on a tape recorder.

8. Everyone gasped in fear when one of the officers _____ that the murderer would probably strike again before the week was over.

6   **Words Beginning with *per-*.** Use the words at the left to fill in the blanks.

per cent
perfect
perform
performers
perfume
perhaps
permitted
perspired

1. It was a _____ July evening in the small town.

2. Gazing out at the crowd, the manager guessed that well over fifty

   _____ of the townspeople had decided to spend the evening at the concert hall.

3. The concert was to begin in twenty minutes, and one of the female

   _____ was very upset.

4. It seemed that the manager had objected to the kind of _____ she was using and ordered her to take a shower at once, or she was out of the show.

5. She, in turn, claimed that she _____ so much when she sang that she had to use this kind.

6. The manager never _____ anyone to argue with him.

7. "_____ you would be happier singing with another group," he said coldly.

8. "I intend to _____ with this group, and nobody is going to stop me," she snapped back, and she was right—nobody was able to stop her.

Review: Lessons 1-8

1 **Word Study.** Put the letter of the answer that best matches the meaning of the underlined word or words on the line to the left.

_____ 1. Andy had been <u>deathly afraid</u> of snakes ever since his sister had thrown one at him at a birthday party one summer.

    (a) a little scared   (c) very scared

    (b) not scared at all   (d) somewhat scared

_____ 2. The <u>value</u> of the diamond necklace was two thousand dollars.

    (a) cost   (b) price   (c) treasure   (d) worth

_____ 3. Mr. Mansfield was in such a hurry that he <u>scrawled</u> his name on the contract without even reading the fine print.

    (a) inked   (b) printed   (c) scribbled   (d) wrote

_____ 4. The <u>theme</u> of the speaker's talk at the town meeting last Tuesday was the need for more adult reading courses.

    (a) discussion   (c) opening statement

    (b) main idea   (d) truth

_____ 5. When the babysitter noticed how much the children were <u>shuddering</u>, she decided to give her ghost story a happy ending.

    (a) disobeying   (b) shivering   (c) smirking   (d) whispering

_____ 6. Mrs. Frost found a <u>loophole</u> in the contract and refused to sign it.

    (a) way of escape   (c) spelling mistake

    (b) tear   (d) wrong word

_____ 7. Whenever Susan felt her day was going badly, she would <u>recite</u> verses from the Scriptures to steady her nerves.

    (a) recall   (b) say   (c) skim   (d) write down

_____ 8. After having painted the kitchen and the bathroom, Thomas was <u>thoroughly</u> exhausted.

    (a) faintly   (b) mildly   (c) somewhat   (d) totally

_____ 9. Mrs. Martin was so <u>easygoing</u> that her neighbors were convinced that she was not strict enough with her children.

    (a) busy   (b) relaxed   (c) shy   (d) tense

_____ 10. Sue <u>hounded</u> her husband to get a better job.

    (a) begged   (b) hoped   (c) nagged   (d) teased

_____ 11. At the <u>precise</u> moment that Bill arrived at the restaurant, his date, who had gotten tired of waiting, left.

    (a) exact   (b) normal   (c) right   (d) unlucky

_____ 12. Mike seemed <u>poised</u> when he played the piano at the Christmas concert.

    (a) calm   (b) edgy   (c) frightened   (d) not prepared

_____ 13. The schoolteacher explained to the class that many people still live in homes that have <u>thatched</u> roofs.

(a) plate glass   (b) straw   (c) tiled   (d) wood

_____ 14. When he got home from work Monday night, Paul built a <u>hutch</u> for the bunny he had given his grandson for Easter.

(a) den   (b) hut   (c) pen   (d) snare

_____ 15. After having stood in the sun for an hour to salute the troops as they passed by the reviewing stand, the commander felt <u>lightheaded</u>.

(a) blessed   (b) boastful   (c) faint   (d) squeamish

2 **Synonyms.** Match the words at the left with their synonyms.

applaud
christen
clinging
easygoing
permit
perspire
shriek
shriveled
spun
snare
squawk
value

_____ 1. allow

_____ 2. complain

_____ 3. grasping

_____ 4. name

_____ 5. praise

_____ 6. relaxed

_____ 7. scream

_____ 8. shrunken

_____ 9. sweat

_____ 10. trap

_____ 11. whirled

_____ 12. worth

3 **Antonyms.** Match the words at the left with their antonyms.

begin
cleansed
complex
eager
glittery
overjoyed
recline
relaxing
scarce
silent
skimp
youth

_____ 1. adult

_____ 2. conclude

_____ 3. depressed

_____ 4. dull

_____ 5. impure

_____ 6. noisy

_____ 7. simple

_____ 8. splurge

_____ 9. stand

_____ 10. stressful

_____ 11. unwilling

_____ 12. widespread

4 **Review of Word Sounds.** Choose the word in the line that has the same sound as the underlined letters in the first word and write it on the line to the right. Study the example before you begin.

1. **cl<u>ove</u>:**	gl<u>ove</u>	m<u>ove</u>	sh<u>ove</u>	st<u>ove</u>	_stove_
2. **cr<u>ea</u>ky:**	cl<u>ea</u>nser	d<u>ea</u>thly	y<u>ea</u>st	h<u>ea</u>dway	_____
3. **p<u>o</u>st:**	c<u>o</u>st	c<u>o</u>stly	h<u>o</u>st	l<u>o</u>st	_____
4. **tong<u>ue</u>:**	arg<u>ue</u>	d<u>ue</u>s	iss<u>ue</u>s	leag<u>ue</u>	_____
5. **<u>ch</u>ap:**	<u>ch</u>ampagne	<u>ch</u>ildish	<u>Ch</u>icago	Mi<u>ch</u>igan	_____
6. **<u>a</u>rise:**	<u>A</u>pril	<u>a</u>rtery	<u>a</u>venue	<u>a</u>longside	_____
7. **pr<u>ow</u>l:**	gr<u>ow</u>nup	sn<u>ow</u>y	t<u>ow</u>el	well-kn<u>ow</u>n	_____
8. **sw<u>ear</u>:**	b<u>ear</u>d	b<u>ear</u>	<u>ear</u>th	n<u>ear</u>by	_____
9. **<u>ou</u>tlaw:**	s<u>ou</u>p	tr<u>ou</u>ble	y<u>ou</u>rs	playgr<u>ou</u>nd	_____
10. **f<u>ou</u>ntain:**	downp<u>ou</u>r	h<u>ou</u>nd	y<u>ou</u>th	humor<u>ou</u>s	_____

5 **Which Word Fits Best?** Choose the best answer and write it on the line.

1. Before is to after as preview is to _____.
   (a) recovery   (b) regret   (c) reminder   (d) review

2. Perfect is to faulty as airtight is to _____.
   (a) creaky   (b) hazy   (c) leaky   (d) slimy

3. Smuggling is to crime as smallpox is to _____.
   (a) crippled   (b) disease   (c) rash   (d) splotches

4. Check-out counter is to store as tollbooth is to _____.
   (a) avenue   (b) footpath   (c) freeway   (d) turnpike

5. Tweezers are to pluck as skillet is to _____.
   (a) broil   (b) fry   (c) oven   (d) scrambled eggs

6. Hound is to bark as frog is to _____.
   (a) chirp   (b) croak   (c) shriek   (d) tinkle

7. Argue is to fight as ban is to _____.
   (a) cleanse   (b) disagree   (c) disobey   (d) outlaw

8. Squash is to side dish as _____ is to dessert.
   (a) broth   (b) custard   (c) frosting   (d) snack

9. Sell is to druggist as prescribe is to _____.
   (a) coach   (b) nurse   (c) teacher   (d) veterinarian

10. Paris is to France as _____ is to the United States.
    (a) Chicago   (b) Los Angeles   (c) New York City   (d) Washington, D.C.

6 **If You Had the Money** . . . Fill in the blank with the choice you would make if you had the money to spend on these things.

_____ 1. You have three weeks off from work. Would you go to _____?

(a) Africa   (c) England and France

(b) California   (d) New York City

_____ 2. Would you go by _____?

(a) car   (b) hiking   (c) jet   (d) ship   (e) train

_____ 3. Would you stay in a(n) _____?

(a) apartment   (b) campground   (c) hotel   (d) motel

_____ 4. Would you eat most of your meals in _____?

(a) a diner   (c) a snack bar

(b) a restaurant   (d) someone's home

_____ 5. During the day, would you spend most of your time _____?

(a) in a museum   (c) shopping

(b) on a beach   (d) taking walks

_____ 6. During the night, would you spend most of your time _____?

(a) at the movies   (c) reading

(b) in a night club (d) watching television

_____ 7. When you go shopping, would you buy _____?

(a) books and records   (c) gifts for your friends

(b) clothing   (d) jewelry

_____ 8. Would you send your friends _____?

(a) cards   (b) gifts   (c) letters   (d) snapshots

_____ 9. If you go out to eat, would you order _____?

(a) cheeseburgers   (b) lobster   (c) roast beef   (d) steak

_____ 10. For something to drink, would you order _____?

(a) beer   (b) champagne   (c) milk   (d) wine

Word Index: Lessons 1-8

A
airtight
alongside
antonym
applaud
applause
argue
arise
arose
arrest
author
avenue

B
Bacchus
backward
ban
barbecue
bathmat
bathrobe
beech
birthstone
blab
blaze
blessed
blimp
blond(e)
bloodshed
blowtorch
blubber
blueberry
blur
boastful
bonnet
boost
bother
boyfriend
brat
breach
breadbox
brighten
brim
brittle
brood
broth
brushoff
buttermilk

C
carefully
carelessly
castor oil
chairman
champ
chant
chap
chapel
check-out

cherry
Chicago
childish
chock
chooser
Chris
christen
Christ-like
Christopher
chuck
chuckle
clamp
clause
cleanse
cleanser
cleat
clinch
cling
clink
clog
clot
clove
clover
clump
coffeepot
coldly
colorblind
company
contest
cotton
craft
cram
crank
creak
creaky
creed
creek
crest
cripple
croak
crossbar
crossroad
cruel
cue
cuss
custard

D
daze
deathly
decoy
Denver
discussion
disobey
doubt
draft
drawbridge
drawstring

dredge
drifter
drive-in
droop
dropout
druggist
drunken

E
eager
earnings
ease
easygoing
enlarge
envelope
equal
equally
evil
export
eyebrow

F
feedback
first-rate
flabby
flatly
flatter
flattery
flex
flick
floss
flown
flung
follow
follower
footpath
fountain
fraction
fraud
Fred
Frenchman
fret
fringe
fro
frost
frostbite
frosting
fuzz

G
galoshes
gap
gape
gasp
ghost
glassful
glaze

Glen
glider
glittery
glob
glory
glum
goat
granddaughter
grandpa
grandson
grandstand
grasp
grant
grate
grateful
Greenland
greyhound
grim
groin
groove
grope
grubby
gunshot

H
hailstorm
half-wit
hardworking
haste
haze
hazy
headline
headway
heal
he's
hitch
horseshoe
host
hound
humid
humor
humorous
hutch

I
impatience
inner
insurance
intelligent
interest
investment
invitation
issue

J
jewel
jeweler

jig
jiggle
Jimmy
joyfully

K
keen

L
lain
license
lightheaded
lion
loafer
loan shark
loin
loop
loophole
Los Angeles

M
madam
madhouse
mane
Mars
marsh
marshmallow
marshy
master
meantime
member
Midas
mixed
moneybags
moth
mothball
mount
mouthpiece
mustard
mutt

N
necessary
necklace
Nile
northeastern
nosebleed

O
obey
odds
opening
opportunity
outburst
outcry
outdoor
outlaw

overjoyed
overpaid

P
palace
Pan
panhandle
panhandler
Paris
partner
patience
payroll
peak
pencil
per cent
perfect
perfume
permit
perspire
petal
pickup
placement
plainclothes
planter
playmate
playpen
pleasure
pliers
plop
pluck
plumber
poise
poisoner
pose
post
postman
potpie
power
powerhouse
prank
precise
predict
prepare
prescribe
pressure
prevent
preview
prime
princess
prod
prowl
prowler

Q
quiz

R
ranch
rap

reaction
reborn
receipt
recite
recline
recorder
reed
regret
reload
reminder
reorder
replace
replacement
restrain
reverse
review
revolve
revolver
reward
rind
roost
rooster
root
ruby

S

safety
saint
salute
scab
scalp
scarce
scarcely
schoolhouse
schoolroom
schoolteacher
schooner
Scotland
scramble
scrapbook
scrawl
screwball
scribble
Scripture
scum
self-pity
sh!
shabby
shall
shed
shipshape
shiver
shoe
shoelace
shoestring
shoplifting
shortchange

showroom
shriek
shrine
shrivel
shrubbery
shrunken
shudder
silver
sketchbook
sketchy
skillet
skim
skimp
skit
slack
slash
slate
slime
slimy
slingshot
slit
slope
slosh
slug
slur
smallpox
smelly
smirk
smock
smother
smuggle
snack bar
snare
snazzy
snipe
snitch
snowflake
snowy
snuff
solo
somewhere
southwestern
spareribs
spearmint
speedway
spellbound
spike
splashdown
splashy
splatter
splendid
splendidly
splotch
splutter
spotted
sprang
sprig

springtime
sprinkle
spruce
sprung
spun
spur
squad
squawk
squash
squeamish
squid
stab
stack
stag
stagger
steady
steeple
stench
stiff
stock
stole
stoplight
storybook
strangle
strangler
strengthen
strep
stretcher
stride
stringy
strive
strut
stub
suggest
suggestion
Susan
swank
sway
sweat shirt
swelling
swimsuit
switchblade
swollen
swore
synonym

T

tango
taut
taxi
thank you
thatched
thee
theirs
theme
thereabout
thereafter

they'd
they'll
thickness
thigh
thorough
thoroughly
thrash
thresh
thresher
thriller
throttle
throwaway
thruway
tinkle
toad
toilet
toll
tollbooth
torch
totally
tract
trade-in
train wreck
traitor
treasure
treaty
trench
trespass
troublesome
turnpike
twang
tweed
tweezers
twentieth
twig
twitch

U

unequal
uniform
unlighted
unlock
unnecessary
unsteady

V

vain
value
vast
velvet
vent
vet
veteran
veterinarian

W

Washington, D.C.
weakness

welcome
well-to-do
wept
we've
wheelchair
whereabouts
whiplash
whirlpool
whisper
whistle
White House
whop
whopper
wick
wishbone
wishy-washy
wit
withdraw
wrestle

X

Y

yeast
yoke
yours
youth

Z

zebra

Lesson 9

Review of Vowel Combinations: Part 2

ai:	wail	frail	Maine	mayonnaise	straightforward
ēa:	lease	cease	ceasefire	treason	
ĕa:	head-on	headlight	ready-made	ready-to-wear	
ee:	keenly	freehand	free-for-all	Halloween	
oa:	foam	roam	hoax	carload	charcoal
oi:	oily	ointment	appoint	appointment	disappoint
oy:	employ	employee	annoy	soy	
oo:	loot	coon	doom	roomy	roomful
ou:	bout	aloud	doubtful	loudmouth	
ui:	lawsuit	unsuited	fruitful	fruity	

1 **Word Meanings.** Use the words at the left to fill in the blanks.

annoy
cease
doubtful
frail
free-for-all
Halloween
lease
loot
Maine
ointment
soy
treason
unsuited
wail

_____ 1. a bean widely grown to improve the soil and feed livestock; also used to make a sauce

_____ 2. a contract that a landlord or landlady gives you when you rent an apartment

_____ 3. a fight in which many people take part; also a contest or race that anyone may enter

_____ 4. a New England state

_____ 5. not fit for a certain job or task

_____ 6. stolen goods; also a slang term for money

_____ 7. the eve of All Saint's Day, falling on October 31, and celebrated by children who go from door to door begging treats or playing pranks

_____ 8. the crime committed by a traitor

_____ 9. something put on the skin to heal a burn, bruise, etc.

_____ 10. to bother someone

_____ 11. to make a sad, crying sound

_____ 12. to put an end to; to stop

_____ 13. unsure or uncertain

_____ 14. weak; not strong

Words for Study

Parsons	ain't	insane	disasters
battered	wooden	Westbury	insured
clack	mister	explosion	vats

A Man Who Had No Eyes

A beggar was coming down the avenue just as Mr. Parsons was coming out of the hotel. He was a blind beggar, carrying a battered cane and thumping his way before him with caution. He was a shaggy man; his coat was greasy and he had a black pouch slung over his shoulder. It seemed that he had something to sell.

The air was rich with spring; the sun was warm and yellowed on the sidewalk. Mr. Parsons, standing there in front of his hotel and noting the clack-clack sound of the blind man's cane, felt a quick and foolish sort of pity for all the blind.

And, thought Mr. Parsons, he was very glad to be alive. A few years ago he had been little more than a skilled worker. Now he was a successful and respected insurance salesman. And he had done it alone, without help, and struggling beneath handicaps. And he was still young.

He took a step forward just as the tap-tapping blind man passed by. Quickly, the shabby man turned. "Listen, man. Just a minute of your time."

Mr. Parsons said, "It's late. I have an appointment. Do you want me to give you something?"

"I ain't no beggar, man. You bet I ain't. I got a handy little thing here"—he groped about until he could press a small object into Mr. Parsons's hand—"that I sell. One buck. Best cigarette lighter made."

Mr. Parsons stood there, somewhat annoyed. He was a handsome man with his gray suit and gray hat and wooden cane. Of course the man with the cigarette lighters could not see him . . . "But I don't smoke," he said.

"Listen. I bet you know a lot of people who smoke. Nice little present. And, mister, you wouldn't mind helping a poor guy out?" He clung to Mr. Parsons's sleeve.

Mr. Parsons sighed and felt in his vest pocket. He brought out two half dollars and pressed them into the man's hand. "Certainly, I'll help you out,"

he said. Then he paused, not wishing to be nosy, even with a blind beggar. "Have you lost your sight completely?"

The shabby man pocketed the two half dollars. "Fourteen years, man." Then he added with an insane sort of pride, "Westbury, sir. I was one of them."

"Westbury," repeated Mr. Parsons. "Oh, yes. The chemical explosion. The papers haven't mentioned it for years. But at the time, it was one of the greatest disasters in—"

"They've all forgot about it," the beggar cried. "But I tell you, man. A man who was in it don't forget about it. Last thing I ever saw was C shop going up in one grand smudge, and that awful gas pouring in at all the busted windows."

Mr. Parsons coughed. But the blind beggar was caught up in remembering the disaster. Also, he was thinking that there might be more half dollars in Mr. Parsons's pocket.

"Just think about it, man. There was a hundred and eight people killed, about two hundred injured, and over fifty of them lost their eyes. Blind as bats." He groped forward until his dirty hand rested against Mr. Parsons's coat. "I tell you, sir, there wasn't nothing worse than that in the war. If I had lost my eyes in the war, okay. I would have been well took care of. But I was just a workman, and I got it. You're darn right I got it, while the bigwigs were making their dough! They was insured, don't worry about that. They—"

"Insurance," repeated Mr. Parsons. "Yes. That's what I sell."

"You want to know how I lost my eyes?" cried the beggar. "Well, here it is! I was in C shop, last of all the folks rushing out. Out in the air there was a chance, even with the buildings exploding right and left. A lot of guys made it safe out the door and got away. Just when I was about to the door, crawling along between those big vats, a guy behind me grabs my legs. He hauls me back and climbs right over me! Shoves me into the dirt. He gets out, and I lie there with all that poison gas pouring down on all sides of me. That's the story, man."

"Not quite," said Mr. Parsons.

The blind beggar shivered. "Not quite? What do you mean?"

"The story is true," Mr. Parsons said, "except that it was the other way around."

"Other way around?" The beggar growled in an unfriendly voice. "Say, man—"

"I was in C shop," said Mr. Parsons. "It was the other way around. You were the man who hauled back on me and climbed over me. You were bigger than I was, Marks."

The blind man stood for a long time, swallowing quickly. He gulped: "Parsons. By God! By God! I thought you—" And then he screamed: "Yes. Maybe so. Maybe so. But I'm blind! I'm blind, and you've been standing here letting me spout off to you and laughing at me every minute! I'm blind."

People in the street turned to stare at him.

"You got away, but I'm blind! Do you hear? I'm—"

"Well," said Mr. Parsons, "don't make such a big deal about it, Marks . . . So am I."

MacKinlay Kantor, ''A Man Who Had No Eyes,'' adapted and reprinted by permission of Paul R. Reynolds, Inc. © 1931 Liberty Magazine.

2 **About the Story.** Choose the answer that best completes the sentence and write it on the line.

1. This story takes place_____.
   (a) in a chemical plant
   (b) in a hotel
   (c) in Westbury
   (d) on a sidewalk

2. This story takes place in _____.
   (a) autumn
   (b) spring
   (c) summer
   (d) winter

3. Mr. Parsons sells _____.
   (a) chemicals
   (b) cigarette lighters
   (c) insurance
   (d) vats

4. One of Marks's first reasons for telling Mr. Parsons the details of the chemical explosion is _____

   (a) he needs to talk in order to overcome his depression
   (b) he thinks Mr. Parsons might give him more money
   (c) he wants to inform Mr. Parsons of the working conditions in Westbury
   (d) this is the way he is used to spending his time

5. When Mr. Parsons exposes Marks's lie, Marks's first excuse is _____

_____ .

   (a) he didn't know his story was phony until Mr. Parsons set him straight on the facts
   (b) he has ended up blind, but at least Mr. Parsons can see
   (c) he was trying to make the story more interesting
   (d) life has been so hard that he had no other choice

6. The people on the street have stopped and are staring because _____

_____ .

   (a) Marks is screaming
   (b) Marks looks so shabby
   (c) the men are blind
   (d) people are nosy

7. The word that best describes Mr. Parsons is _____ .

   (a) angry
   (b) depressed
   (c) nosy
   (d) successful

8. The word that best describes Marks is _____ .

   (a) cheerful
   (b) frail
   (c) self-pitying
   (d) straightforward

9. Besides selling cigarette lighters, Marks is also _____ .

   (a) a bigwig
   (b) an insurance salesman
   (c) a veteran
   (d) a workman

10. A word that means almost the same as *parson* is _____ .

   (a) insurance salesman
   (b) lawyer
   (c) preacher
   (d) teacher

3 **About the Story.** Answer these questions.

1. Many short stories have surprise endings. What is the surprise ending in "A Man Who Had No Eyes"?

_____

_____

2. Why do you think Mr. Parsons has become successful while Marks begs for a living?

_____

_____

_____

4 **Who Are These People?** Use the words at the left to fill in the blanks.

jeweler
looter
porter
printer
producer
rancher
sniper
surfer
treasurer
trespasser
trooper
wrestler

_____ 1. A newspaper hires this person to work the press.

_____ 2. A railroad hires this person to carry suitcases and heavy bags.

_____ 3. This person breaks into stores or homes and steals others' belongings.

_____ 4. This person commits a sin or invades the property or rights of another without his consent.

_____ 5. This person is in charge of the money or funds for a business, club, etc.

_____ 6. This person issues tickets to drivers who exceed the speed limit.

_____ 7. This person makes films for movie houses or TV.

_____ 8. This person owns or runs a huge farm on which large herds of cattle, sheep, or horses are raised.

_____ 9. This person sells wristwatches, necklaces, bracelets, etc.

_____ 10. This person shoots at other people from a concealed place.

_____ 11. This person's goal is to pin the other person on the mat until he's declared the winner.

_____ 12. You can find this person on the beach carrying a board under his arm.

5 **Common Word Beginnings.** Answer these questions on the lines.

_____ 1. If you don't show up on time for a date, do you *appoint* or *disappoint* someone?

_____ 2. If you were to meet a well-known movie star, would you be *depressed, impressed,* or *repressed*?

_____ 3. To which do you respond better—*insults* or *results*?

_____ 4. Is cigarette smoking *healthy* or *unhealthy*?

_____ 5. Are your earnings called *income* or *outcome*?

_____ 6. Do most children ask their older brothers or sisters to *deflate* or *inflate* a balloon for them?

_____ 7. Can an insect bite become *dejected, infected,* or *rejected*?

_____ 8. Is Friday the thirteenth thought to be a *lucky* or an *unlucky* day?

_____ 9. Does the United States *export* or *import* most of its oil?

_____ 10. Are you completing this lesson with *impatience* or *patience*?

6 **Can You Crack the Code?** Each word relates to the theme listed above the words, but the words have been concealed by a code.

A. In the code, a new set of letters has been used in place of the normal letters. For example, in the code below, *h* is used in place of *o, a* is used in place of *n, n* is used in place of *i,* and *x* is used in place of *s.* The code is the same for all the words.

B. To break the code, fill in the *o*'s, *i*'s, *n*'s, and *s*'s. Then think about things you can put on a sandwich. Also watch for how often a letter appears. For example, in #6, *m* appears three times, so *m* is probably the code letter for a letter that appears often in English words.

C. When you have guessed a word, use these letters for the other words until you have cracked the code for the entire group.

Theme: Something to put on your sandwich.

        O   N   I   O   N S
1. H A N H A X

2. Q J X F G D I

3. Q G R H A A G N X M

4. S N K Z V M X

5. Z M F K U J S

6. K U M M X M

7. S M G A J F   E J F F M D

8. L M V V R

9. L G Q

10. F H Q G F H M X

Lesson 10

Review of *r*-Controlled Vowels

ar:	spar	sparkle	Carl	marker	market	argument
are:	mare	nightmare	blare	ware	day-care	carfare
er:	fern	stern	eastern	western	jersey	New Jersey
ir:	shirk	twirl	rebirth	birthplace	dirt-cheap	first aid
or:	fore	forehead	sorehead	moreover	pore	orderly
ur:	urge	urgent	urgently	burnt	purple	surround

1 **Word Meanings.** Use the words at the left to fill in the blanks.

fern
first aid
jersey
mare
market
New Jersey
nightmare
pore
purple
shirk
sorehead
spar
sparkle
stern
urgent

——————————— 1. a dark color that is a blend of red and blue; in the old days, the color of royalty or high rank

——————————— 2. a female horse

——————————— 3. a frightening dream

——————————— 4. a knitted pullover shirt worn for certain sports

——————————— 5. a person who gets very angry when he is defeated

——————————— 6. a plant

——————————— 7. a store or shop where items such as meat are sold

——————————— 8. a tiny opening in the skin through which liquids may be taken in or discharged

——————————— 9. an eastern state in the United States

——————————— 10. firm or strict

——————————— 11. needing or demanding prompt action

——————————— 12. to avoid doing something that should be done

——————————— 13. to box with skill and some caution, landing a few heavy blows

——————————— 14. to glitter or shine like jewels, wet grass in the sun, etc.

——————————— 15. treatment given in case of injury or sudden sickness

Words for Study

Louis Braille	features	project	possible
dorm	tangled	system	beyond
stylus	cheekbones	forever	hoofs

Louis Braille as a Youth

The dorm was dark and still. Only one boy was awake. He sat on the edge of his bed at a far corner of the room, holding a sheet of thick paper on his lap. Slowly, he punched tiny holes across the page with the point of a sharp stylus. Every few minutes he paused, ran his fingers across the raised dots on the other side of the paper, then continued working with his stylus.

A deep whisper coming from the next bed stopped him for a minute. "Louis? That you? Still punching dots?"

"Sh! Be still. It's late. You'll wake up everyone," Louis replied.

"You'd better quit and get some rest, Louis. The teacher will be really angry if you doze off in class again."

"I know. I know. I'm almost through now. Please, go back to sleep."

Louis Braille placed his paper and stylus on a shelf behind his bed. Extending his arm before him, he walked across the dorm and stood before an open window. He was a thin boy, but handsome, with sharp, intelligent features which made him seem somewhat older than his fifteen years. Tangled blond hair fell over his large forehead. His features were hurt only by his eyes which stared blankly from above his cheekbones.

Louis was a student at a school for blind youth in Paris. For months now, he had been working intensely on a project which had come to rule his entire life. He was trying to work out a system of reading and writing for the blind. This system was based on combining dots which were punched into paper with a sharp, pointed tool called a stylus.

As it was, the blind had no means of reading or writing. The best system that had been invented for them to date was almost useless. Because of this, they could not hope to share fully in life. Young Louis refused to accept this fact. He would not admit that because he was blind, he was forever cut off from the rest of the world.

Yet his work with raised dots had not been successful. It was not possible, they said, to invent a truly good system of reading and writing for the blind. Everyone at the school told Louis that he was wasting his time. Lately, the young student had become depressed. He wondered if his project was beyond him. Perhaps it was true—perhaps neither he nor any other blind person could ever take his place in the world of seeing.

From the street below, Louis heard the sound of wheels and the clicking of horses' hoofs. Suddenly, he felt lonely and homesick. He sat down on the rough floor beneath the window, drew his knees up to his chest and leaned his head against the wall. A warm April breeze swept through the room, reminding him of spring in his own town.

At home, the fields now would feel moist and soft beneath his bare feet. The hills would be filled with the smell of new clover. The farmers would soon be bringing their first fruits and vegetables to market in the town square. Reaching further and further back into his childhood, Louis tried to remember what the square had looked like. But he knew it was useless. He had tried to remember so many times before. He could not remember what his house looked like, nor could he picture the faces of his mother and father. The sounds and smells of home—all these were clear, but the sights had faded completely. He could remember nothing he had ever seen. He had been blind much too long.

Adapted with permission of the author, Russell Freedman, from *Teenagers Who Made History.*

2 **About the Story.** Choose the answer that best completes the sentence and write it on the line.

1. This story takes place in a _____ .
   (a) home
   (b) hospital
   (c) museum
   (d) school

2. In what season does this story take place? _____
   (a) autumn
   (b) spring
   (c) summer
   (d) winter

3. The teacher was angry with Louis because _____ .
   (a) he fell asleep in class
   (b) he has not been doing his homework
   (c) he is a rude student
   (d) he is trying to invent a new system of reading and writing for the blind

4. The other people seem to think that Louis's project is _____ .
   (a) hopeful
   (b) important
   (c) successful
   (d) useless

5. In this story, Louis's work on inventing a system of reading and writing for the blind

   is _____ .
   (a) completed
   (b) respected
   (c) successful
   (d) unsuccessful

6. In this story, Louis is feeling _____ .
   (a) dejected
   (b) hopeful
   (c) insulted
   (d) proud

7. Louis could remember _____ .
   (a) all of the sights from his childhood
   (b) none of the sights from his childhood
   (c) some of the sights from his childhood
   (d) only what his mother and father looked like

8. Louis Braille would not admit that _____ .
   (a) he could not remember what his mother looked like
   (b) he had to be cut off from the rest of the world because of his blindness
   (c) he was blind
   (d) the teacher would be angry with him

9. According to this story, the greatest problem confronting the blind at that time was that they were

not able to _____ .
   - (a) enjoy the beauties of nature
   - (b) get around by themselves
   - (c) relate to others through the written word
   - (d) see their families and friends

10. This story was probably meant to inspire us to _____

_____ .
   - (a) enjoy being able to see
   - (b) keep working even when things seem hopeless
   - (c) overcome our fear of blindness
   - (d) respect every person who is blind

3   **More Facts about Louis Braille.** Use the words at the left to complete these sentences.

accident
army
fifteen
Frenchman
idea
machine
messages
Paris
praise
system
1824
1829

Louis Braille (1809-1852) was a blind _____ who invented the braille

_____ of printing and writing for the blind.

Three years after his birth near _____, an _____ blinded

him. He entered a school for the blind when he was ten.

In _____, when Braille was _____ years old, he invented his raised

dot-dash reading system. The _____ came to him from the dot-dash code punched

on cardboard that an _____ officer used to send _____ to his men

at night.

Later, in _____, Braille completed his dot system. This code was not accepted

at once, but it later won the world's _____ . A blind person writes braille on a

6-key _____ called a braillewriter.

4 **Compound Words.** To find the answers, choose a word from **List A** and add a word from **List B** to it.

List A
blood
broom
butter
cotton
fore
jelly
market
post
pot
silver
ware
wood

List B
beans
cards
casts
chuck
holder
hound
house
mouth
place
scotch
sticks
ware

_____ 1. Be sure to use this when you remove a very hot saucepan from the burner.

_____ 2. Children often find these in their Easter baskets.

_____ 3. Commonly found in northern and eastern North America, this animal has short legs, a heavyset body and brown fur.

_____ 4. Hunters find this breed of dog useful because of its keen sense of smell.

_____ 5. Many children believe that witches ride these on Halloween.

_____ 6. People who want to know what the weather is going to be like follow these reports closely.

_____ 7. This is an open square or other place where people can buy goods.

_____ 8. This is one kind of sauce that people enjoy pouring over their ice cream.

_____ 9. This poisonous snake can be found in the swamps of the southern United States.

_____ 10. When a family moves, they often store their belongings here until they find a new home.

_____ 11. When company is coming for dinner, the host sets his table with this.

_____ 12. When people are away from home, they often send these to their friends.

5 **More Work with Word Beginnings.** Answer these questions on the lines.

_____ 1. If an army is losing a battle, does it *mistreat* or *retreat*?

_____ 2. If you want to have good health, is it *necessary* or *unnecessary* to eat white sugar?

_____ 3. Are men and women who have celebrated their sixty-fifth birthdays normally *employed* or *unemployed*?

_____ 4. Do police officers arrest people for *disorderly* or *orderly* conduct?

_____ 5. When you see someone cry, are you *affected* or *unaffected*?

_____ 6. Do you try to do your shopping at stores that offer *discounts* or *miscounts*?

_____ 7. When you can't remember something that you really want to remember, do you try to *miscall* or *recall* it?

_____ 8. Do you like your hamburgers *overdone* or *underdone*?

_____ 9. Does a speaker try to make a *compact* or an *impact* upon the people to whom he is speaking?

_____ 10. Do you *inspect* or *respect* your close friends?

_____ 11. If you obey an order, do you *comply* with it or *reply* to it?

_____ 12. If you have just drunk three glasses of champagne, is your walk *steady* or *unsteady*?

6 **Syllables.** Write each word, in syllables, on the lines to the right. Study the example before you begin.

1. treatment *treat·ment* _____

2. sickness _____

3. sorehead _____

4. roomful _____

5. rebirth _____

6. livestock _____

7. compact _____

8. member _____

9. project _____

10. insure _____

11. headlight _____

12. lesson _____

13. keenly _____

14. charcoal _____

15. annoy _____

16. appointment _____

Lesson 11

The Hard and Soft *c*

In these words, the **c** is hard as in <u>c</u>amp, <u>c</u>ontest, and <u>c</u>urve.
(The hard **c** sounds like a **k**.)

cask	catchy	calf	coop	cucumber
casket	category	capital	coffin	Cuba
cabin	carton	capitalize	Columbus	cuddle
cabinet	cartoon	carrot	Colorado	

In these words, the **c** is soft as in <u>c</u>enter, <u>c</u>ity, and jui<u>c</u>e.
(The soft **c** sounds like an **s**.)

cite	ceaseless	niece	decent	cinnamon
incite	deceased	apiece	indecent	Cincinnati
citizen	decision	Nancy	decently	
citizenship	incision	mercy	recent	

1 **Word Meanings.** Use the words at the left to fill in the blanks.

calf
carrot
casket
catchy
Cincinnati
cinnamon
Columbus
coop
Cuba
cucumber
cuddle
deceased
incision
incite
mercy
niece

_____ 1. a cut into the soft tissues of the body made by a doctor

_____ 2. a daughter of one's brother or brother-in-law, or sister or sister-in-law

_____ 3. a synonym for coffin

_____ 4. a tree from which the bark is dried and ground into a spice

_____ 5. a vegetable, often found in salads, that "helps to keep you cool"

_____ 6. a yellow vegetable that is good for your eyes

_____ 7. a willingness to be kind and forgiving toward others

_____ 8. a young cow or bull; also, the back part of the leg between the knee and the ankle

_____ 9. where chickens and hens live

_____ 10. no longer living; dead

_____ 11. the capital of Ohio; also, the last name of the explorer who sailed to America in 1492

_____ 12. a city located on the Ohio River

_____ 13. an island country located south of Florida.

_____ 14. a word which describes something easily remembered

_____ 15. to hug somebody

_____ 16. to urge or to stir up action

Words for Study

soul	supper	peddler	prison
tempted	tobacco	thrust	darkness
pastime	good-by	realized	mill

The Rat Trap: Part I

Once upon a time there was a man who went around selling small rat traps. This business did not bring him much money, so he had to fall back on begging and stealing to keep body and soul together. Even so, his clothes were in rags, and hunger gleamed in his eye.

One day, this man was thinking of his rat traps when suddenly he was struck by the idea that the whole world was nothing but a big rat trap. It had never existed for any other reason than to set bait for people. It offered riches and joys exactly as the rat trap offered cheese, and as soon as anyone let himself be tempted to touch the bait, it closed in on him, and then everything came to an end.

The world had, of course, never been very kind to him, so it gave him great joy to think badly of it in this way. It became a treasured pastime of his, during his long days on the road, to think of people he knew who had let themselves be caught in the dangerous snare, and of others who were still circling around the bait.

One dark evening as he was trudging along the road, he caught sight of a little gray house by the roadside. He knocked on the door to ask shelter for the night. He was not refused. Instead of sour faces which greeted him most of the time, the owner, a lonely old man without wife or child, was happy to have someone to talk to. He put the stew pot on the fire at once and gave him supper. Then he carved off such a big slice from his tobacco roll that it was enough for both the stranger's pipe and his own. He then got out an old pack of cards and played cards with his guest until bedtime.

The old man told his guest of the job he had at the iron mill when he was younger. And he told of his cow whose milk he sold. He was paid thirty dollars a month for the milk.

To prove he was telling the truth, the old man got up and went to the window, took down a leather pouch which hung on a nail, and picked out three ten-dollar bills. These he held up before the eyes of his guest and then stuffed them back into his pouch.

The next day both men got up early. The old man was in a hurry to milk his cow, and the other man thought he should not stay in bed when the head of the house had gotten up. The man with the rat traps said good-by and thank you, and each went his own way.

But half an hour later the rat trap peddler stood again before the door. He did not try to get in, however. He only went up to the window, smashed a pane, stuck in a hand, and got hold of the pouch with the thirty dollars. He took the money and thrust it into his own pocket. Then he hung the leather pouch carefully back in its place and went away.

As he walked along with the money in his pocket, he felt quite pleased with himself. He knew that at first he dared not continue on the highway, but must turn off the road into the woods. During the first few hours this caused him no trouble. Later in the day it became worse, for the forest he had gotten into was big and confusing. He walked and walked without coming to the end of the wood, and then he realized that he had been walking around in the same part of the forest. All at once he recalled his thoughts about the world and the rat trap. Now his own turn had come. He had let himself be fooled by bait and had been caught. The whole forest, with its trunks and branches and fallen logs, closed in upon him like a prison from which he could never escape.

It was late December. Darkness was already falling. This increased the danger and also increased his gloom. At last he saw no way out, and he sank down on the ground, tired to death, thinking that his last moment had come. But just as he laid his head on the ground, he heard a sound—a hard, steady thumping. There was no doubt as to what that was. He raised himself. "Those are the hammer strokes from an iron mill," he thought. "There must be people nearby." He called upon all his strength and staggered toward the sound.

Continued in the next lesson . . .

Adaptation of "The Rat Trap" from *Harvest* by Selma Lagerlof, translated by Florence and Neboth Hedin. Copyright 1934, 1935 by Doubleday & Company, Inc. Reprinted by permission of the publisher.

2 **About the Story**. Answer these questions.

1. Cite three ways in which the peddler gets his money.

a. _____

b. _____

c. _____

2. In your own words, explain the peddler's idea about what life is like.

_____

_____

_____

3. Why does the peddler believe life is like this?

_____

_____

4. Why is the old man so eager for the peddler's company?

_____

5. How does the peddler get himself caught in a "rat trap"?

_____

_____

6. Do you agree or disagree with the peddler's idea about life? Give at least one example to explain what you think about this.

_____

_____

_____

3 **What Is a Soul?** Use the words at the left to fill in the blanks.

act
animal
believed
body
cleansed
example
faiths
lifetime
next
return

Most people who have faith in God or gods believe that there is something in man

that lives after the _____ itself has died. This is the soul.

In some _____, it is believed that the soul is reborn into bodies many times

until it is _____ enough to return to God.

It is also _____ by some people that the kinds of things a person does in

a _____ decide his fate. For _____, if a man chooses to live

like an animal, he will _____ to earth as an _____.

Thus, how you _____ in one life will decide what you will be in the _____.

4 **Which Answer Fits Best?** Complete each statement with the choice that makes the most sense.

1. Princess is to prince as _____.
   - (a) dancer is to actor
   - (b) king is to queen
   - (c) waiter is to waitress
   - (d) waitress is to waiter

2. Dejected is to blue as _____.
   - (a) black is to white
   - (b) brave is to yellow
   - (c) candy is to purple
   - (d) mad is to red

3. Columbus is to Ohio as _____.
   - (a) Denver is to Colorado
   - (b) Detroit is to New Jersey
   - (c) Los Angeles is to Hawaii
   - (d) Washington, D.C. is to Washington

4. Fringe is to outskirts as _____.
   - (a) buildings are to downtown
   - (b) center is to core
   - (c) head is to heart
   - (d) recent is to old

5. Braille is to braille as _____.
   - (a) Babe Ruth is to baseball
   - (b) Bacchus is to wine
   - (c) Edison is to light bulb
   - (d) Washington, D.C. is to Washington

6. French is to toast as _____.
   - (a) England is to muffin
   - (b) English is to muffin
   - (c) France is to beautiful
   - (d) Paris is to wine

7. Butterscotch is to candy as _____.
   - (a) carrot is to salad
   - (b) jellybean is to vanilla
   - (c) spearmint is to chewing gum
   - (d) tobacco is to pipe

8. Florida is to the South as _____.
   - (a) Cincinnati is to the West
   - (b) Maine is to the Midwest
   - (c) New Jersey is to the East
   - (d) Texas is to the North

9. Scour is to pots and pans as _____.
   - (a) cuddle is to cottonmouth
   - (b) floss is to teeth
   - (c) heal is to incision
   - (d) appoint is to President

10. Incite is to conclude as _____.
   - (a) alive is to deceased
   - (b) crazy is to insane
   - (c) retired is to unemployed
   - (d) unsuccessful is to hopeless

5 **Sounds for c.** In most words, when the letter *c* is followed by *a*, *o*, or *u*, it sounds like *k* as in *cat, cot,* or *cut.* In most words, when the letter *c* is followed by *e* or *i*, it sounds like *s* as in *cent* or *city.*

The words listed below follow these rules. If the *c* in these words is followed by *a*, *o*, or *u*, write *k* above it and say the word to yourself. If the *c* is followed by *e* or *i*, write *s* above it and say the word. Study the example before you begin.

1. circus (s, k)

2. company

3. cider

4. cough

5. ceiling

6. dunce

7. decide

8. curly

9. curdle

10. cancer

11. cue

12. force

13. cobweb

14. Cinderella

15. bacon

6 **Categories.** Put the words listed below in the proper categories. Study the example before you begin.

blight	earthquake	hutch	shipwreck
cage	envelope	knife	soupspoon
cinnamon	flood	newsletter	sty
clove	✓fork	nutmeg	tape
coop	gauze	ointment	teaspoon
cotton	ginger	postcard	ticket

Silverware

1. _fork_
2. _____
3. _____
4. _____

First Aid

1. _____
2. _____
3. _____
4. _____

Spices

1. _____
2. _____
3. _____
4. _____

Animal pens

1. _____
2. _____
3. _____
4. _____

Disasters

1. _____
2. _____
3. _____
4. _____

Paper

1. _____
2. _____
3. _____
4. _____

Lesson 12

The Hard and Soft *g*

In these words, the **g** is hard as in *gag, goat, gumdrop,* and *ragged.*

gab	gifted	gig	gamble	hag
gabby	gift-wrap	giggle	gambler	jag
gash	golf	goggles	gallbladder	jagged
gush	goad	gargle		zigzag

In these words, the **g** is soft as in *germ, ginger, page,* and *fudge.*
(The soft **g** sounds like the letter **j**.)

gee-whiz	Georgia	budge	engine	package
gingersnap	gerbil	budget	engineer	manage
gingerly		fussbudget	Genesis	damage

---

1   **Word Meanings.** Use the words at the left to fill in the blanks.

budget
fussbudget
gabby
gallbladder
gamble
gargle
gash
Genesis
gerbil
gingerly
gingersnap
goad
goggles
hag
zigzag

_____ 1. a deep flesh wound; to make a long, deep cut or to slash deeply

_____ 2. a great cooky for dunking in milk

_____ 3. a line or pattern which has two or more sharp turns

_____ 4. a member of the rat family that is often a household pet

_____ 5. a person who whines and complains a lot

_____ 6. a plan for saving and spending money

_____ 7. an ugly, frightful old woman; a witch

_____ 8. carefully; cautiously

_____ 9. located just under the liver in your body, this stores bile

_____ 10. glasses worn to protect against wind, dust, or glare

_____ 11. the first book of the Bible

_____ 12. a word describing someone who talks a lot

_____ 13. to prod; to urge; to incite

_____ 14. to take a chance on something

_____ 15. something helpful to do when you have a sore throat

Words for Study

type	Elizabeth	effort	wealthy
ironmaster	fellow	kindly	friendless
Neil Olson	impossible	character	saintly

The Rat Trap: Part II

Because of all the noise, the blacksmiths did not see that a man had opened the gate and entered the forge. It was normal for poor tramps to be drawn to the forge by the glow of light which escaped through the smudged panes and to come warm themselves in front of the fire. The blacksmiths only glanced at the stranger and went back to their work. He looked the way people of his type always did, with a long beard, dirty, ragged, and with a bunch of rat traps hanging on his chest.

The tramp did not say anything either. He had not come there to talk but only to warm himself and sleep.

In those days, the iron mill was owned by a highly respected ironmaster, whose greatest goal was to ship out good iron to the market. He watched both day and night to see that the work was done as well as possible, and at this very moment he came into the forge to inspect the work. The first thing he saw was the tall tramp. He walked close up to the tramp and looked him over very carefully.

"But of course it is you, Neil Olson!" he said.

The man with the rat traps had never before seen the ironmaster. But he realized that if this fine gentleman thought he was an old friend, he might give him some money.

"Yes," he said. "God knows things have gone downhill with me."

"You should not have left the army," said the ironmaster. "That was the mistake. Well, now of course you will come home with me."

"No, I couldn't think of it!" the tramp replied, looking quite alarmed. He thought of the thirty dollars. To go home with the ironmaster would be like throwing himself into the lion's den.

The ironmaster saw that he must give in for now, but he was set on having his way. Thus, he went home and told his daughter about the man who sold rat traps. Half an hour later she entered the forge. "My name is Elizabeth," said the young girl. "I am so sorry that you are having such a bad time."

She looked at him with love and concern. Then she saw that the man was afraid. "Perhaps he has stolen something or else has escaped from jail," she thought to herself. She then said aloud, "You will be allowed to leave us as freely as you came. Only please stay with us for Christmas Eve."

She said this in such a friendly manner that the rat trap peddler trusted her and agreed to go with her. But, later, while he was riding up to the house, he felt uneasy. "Why did I take that fellow's money?" he thought. "Now I am sitting in the trap and will never get out of it."

At the house, the tramp was bathed and dressed in one of the ironmaster's best suits. When the ironmaster saw the tramp in full daylight, it was impossible to mistake him for an old friend. "What does this mean?" he thundered.

The stranger made no effort to lie. "It is not my fault, sir," he said. "I never pretended to be anything but a poor trader, and I begged to stay in the forge. But no harm has been done. I can put on my rags again and go away."

Just as he was opening the door, the daughter said, "I think he ought to stay with us today. I don't think we ought to chase away a human being to whom we have offered Christmas cheer." The young girl took the stranger's hand and led him to the table. "Now sit down and eat," she said, for she could see that her father had given in.

The man with the rat traps did not answer anything to this. He only stared at the girl in wonder.

The next morning the ironmaster and his daughter got up to go to church. Their guest was still asleep, and they did not disturb him.

As they drove back from church, the young girl sat and hung her head sadly, for at church she had learned that the old iron worker had been robbed by somebody selling rat traps.

They had hardly gotten home when the ironmaster, who was very angry, asked the maid whether the stranger was still there. The maid answered that the fellow had gone and that he had left behind a Christmas present for his daughter.

The young girl opened the present and gave a little cry of joy. She found a small rat trap, and in it lay three ten-dollar bills. But that was not all. In the rat trap lay also a letter:

Honored Miss:

You can give back the money to the old man on the roadside, who has the money pouch hanging on the window frame as bait for poor tramps.

The rat trap is a Christmas present from a rat who would have been caught in this world's rat trap if he had not been treated so kindly, because in that way he got power to clear himself.

Written with friendship and high regard,

"Neil Olson"

Adaptation of "The Rat Trap" from *Harvest* by Selma Lagerlof, translated by Florence and Neboth Hedin. Copyright 1934, 1935 by Doubleday & Company, Inc. Reprinted by permission of the publisher.

2 **About the Story.** Put the letter of the correct answer on the line to the left.

_____ 1. The blacksmiths do not see the peddler enter the forge because _____.

    (a) he is sneaky
    (b) it is so noisy
    (c) it is too dark
    (d) they are too busy

_____ 2. It is _____ for strangers to come into the forge.

    (a) common   (c) frightening
    (b) dangerous   (d) rare

_____ 3. It is likely that the ironmaster had known Neil Olson _____.

    (a) as an old friend of the family's
    (b) during his childhood
    (c) during the war
    (d) in business

_____ 4. The ironmaster realizes that he has made a mistake when _____.

    (a) he hears the peddler talk
    (b) he sees the peddler dressed in decent clothes
    (c) he sees the peddler in full daylight
    (d) the peddler refuses to go home with him

_____ 5. The first person to realize that the peddler is in some kind of trouble is _____.

    (a) Elizabeth   (c) the ironmaster
    (b) the blacksmiths   (d) the maid

_____ 6. Elizabeth and her father learn that the peddler stole the old man's money _____.

    (a) at home   (c) on Christmas Day
    (b) at the forge   (d) on Christmas Eve

_____ 7. The peddler signs the note with the name "Neil Olson" because _____.

    (a) he doesn't want to reveal his real name
    (b) he thinks he's just as good as Neil Olson
    (c) he wants to make the ironmaster angry
    (d) the daughter has made him feel like Neil Olson

_____ 8. We can guess that the ironmaster _____.

    (a) loves his daughter very much
    (b) sees his daughter as just another mouth to feed
    (c) thinks his daughter is crazy
    (d) wants his daughter to get married

_____ 9. The lesson we can learn from this story is that _____.

    (a) if you tempt somebody with money, he'll always take the bait
    (b) it doesn't pay to help people out
    (c) people act more decently when they are treated decently
    (d) you can't trust anybody

3 **Describing the Characters.** Match each word at the left with the character in "The Rat Trap" it best describes. Use each word only once.

bitter
concerned
friendless
hardworking
lonely
respected
retired
robbed
saintly
tempted
wealthy
young

The peddler

1. _____

2. _____

3. _____

Elizabeth

1. _____

2. _____

3. _____

The ironmaster

1. _____

2. _____

3. _____

The old man

1. _____

2. _____

3. _____

4 **Which Word Does Not Fit?** Choose the word in the line that does not fit with the rest and write it to the right.

1. Texas	Chicago	Detroit	Cincinnati	Los Angeles	_____
2. sir	fellow	male	mister	employee	_____
3. gleam	shine	glitter	sparkle	splendid	_____
4. calf	camel	colt	lamb	puppy	_____
5. street	highway	thruway	roadside	turnpike	_____
6. bile	stomach	pancreas	intestines	gallbladder	_____
7. Asia	Cuba	Holland	Ireland	Spain	_____
8. goal	basket	home run	strikeout	touchdown	_____
9. nag	whiner	crybaby	smuggler	fussbudget	_____
10. good-bye	farewell	so long	good night	you're welcome	_____
11. beet	carrot	eggplant	cranberry	cucumber	_____
12. rough	crooked	jagged	smooth	uneven	_____
13. looter	mugger	traitor	trespasser	loudmouth	_____
14. goad	incite	insult	prod	urge	_____
15. clause	contract	lease	pact	agreement	_____

5 **Sounds for g.** In most words, when the letter g is followed by a, o, or u, it sounds like the g in *gag*, *got*, or *gum*. In many words, when the letter g is followed by e or i, it sounds like j as in *germ* or *gin*.

The words listed below follow these rules. If the g in these words is followed by a, o, or u, write g above it and say the word to yourself. If the g is followed by e or i, write j above it and say the word. Study the example before you begin.

1. garbage   6. gown   11. gobble

2. guilty   7. gorge   12. gentle

3. ginger   8. George   13. drawbridge

4. Chicago   9. urgently   14. gauze

5. gutter   10. gap   15. barge

6 Words Beginning with *dis*- Use the words at the left to fill in the blanks.

disabled
disappointed
disclosed
discovery
diseased
disgrace
disgracefully
disorderly
disperse

1. The Saturday morning paper _____ the fact that the president of the city's largest firm, Herman Frank, had been arrested for drunken and

   _____ conduct.

2. Frank _____ two police officers before other officers managed

   to handcuff him and _____ the crowd that had formed to
   watch the excitement.

3. "What a _____!" exclaimed the citizens to each other as the

   _____ of what had happened spread like wildfire through
   the town.

4. "How could that man be president of anything?" complained one old busybody.

   "He clearly has a _____ mind."

5. In church the next morning, everyone was aware of the Frank family who could
   feel themselves being stared at as if they were the ones who had acted

   _____.

6. The townspeople were _____ when everything settled down;
   nothing this exciting had happened in more than fifty years!

Review: Lessons 1-12

1   **Word Study.** Each of the five words listed at the left has two meanings. Use each word *twice* to fill in the blanks. In some cases, you need to add *-ed* to the word.

calf
draft
grate
stern
type

1. A _____ of cool air is always welcome during a heat wave.

2. Bart's _____ muscle in his left leg was throbbing so badly that he knew he wouldn't be able to start the game.

3. Chris knew that he would be hired because he could _____ faster than anyone else in the class.

4. Elizabeth emptied all the ashtrays in the _____ of the dining room fireplace because she was too lazy to go back to the kitchen.

5. In the 1960's, many young men either left the country or went to prison in order

   to avoid being _____ into the army.

6. Mr. Silvers was so _____ with his five daughters that before they had completed high school, they all ran off to get married just to get out of the house.

7. Rusty hated to go to the beach because the noise from all the radios _____ on his nerves.

8. The entire Barber family searched in vain for the _____ which had strayed from the herd.

9. The front of a ship is called the bow; the rear is called the _____.

10. When Patty asked Tony why he didn't call her anymore, he responded, "Sorry, but

    you're just not my _____."

2   **Word Study.** The five words listed at the left can be said two different ways. Use each word *twice* to fill in the blanks. In some cases, you need to add *-s* or *-ed* to the word.

conduct
content
contest
present
project

1. As the guide _____ the students through the museum, he heard one of them remark, "A monkey can paint better than this!"

2. At the beginning of the pie-eating _____, Joan prayed she would be able to win without getting as sick as she had last year.

3. Eve nearly fainted when the insurance company _____ her with a check for $25,000 to cover the cost of the accident.

4. Even though Dr. Mack seemed to have everything a man could want, he still did not feel _____ with his life.

5. Louis explained to the teacher that nobody at home would help him with his history _____ and that he was afraid he would fail the course.

6. Holly checked the table of _____ to see which page the story started on.

7. The actor decided that if he really wanted to get leading roles, he would have to take voice lessons in order to learn how to _____ his voice.

8. The conductor's brave _____ during the fire, which had started in the baggage car, saved many lives.

9. The workers at the plant all chipped in to buy Gail a wedding _____.

10. When the judge declared, "Out of order," the lawyer jumped to his feet and hotly _____ this decision.

3 Synonyms. Match the words at the left with their synonyms.

apiece
coffin
core
deceased
disclose
employ
frail
fraud
gingerly
pastime
shirk
strangle
thrill
twirl
wail

_____ 1. avoid

_____ 2. casket

_____ 3. cautiously

_____ 4. center

_____ 5. dead

_____ 6. each

_____ 7. excitement

_____ 8. hire

_____ 9. hoax

_____ 10. hobby

_____ 11. moan

_____ 12. reveal

_____ 13. throttle

_____ 14. weak

_____ 15. whirl

4 Antonyms. Match the words at the left with their antonyms.

boost
damage
daylight
diseased
disgrace
evil
gabby
heavyset
humid
insult
vast
veteran

_____ 1. beginner

_____ 2. darkness

_____ 3. dry

_____ 4. healthy

_____ 5. honor

_____ 6. lower

_____ 7. mute

_____ 8. praise

_____ 9. repair

_____ 10. saintly

_____ 11. thin

_____ 12. tiny

5 Review of Word Sounds. Choose the word in the line that has the same sound as the underlined letters in the first word. Study the example before you begin.

1. **bud<u>g</u>e:**   dru<u>gg</u>ist   <u>g</u>amble   <u>G</u>enesis   <u>g</u>o<u>gg</u>les   <u>Genesis</u>

2. **<u>c</u>ite:**   Ba<u>cch</u>us   <u>c</u>arfare   <u>c</u>innamon   re<u>c</u>order   _____

3. **r<u>oo</u>my:**   g<u>oo</u>dbye   gr<u>oo</u>ve   outd<u>oo</u>r   w<u>oo</u>den   _____

4. **cl<u>oth</u>es:**   b<u>oth</u>   br<u>oth</u>   br<u>oth</u>er   m<u>oth</u>   _____

5. **cr<u>oo</u>ked:**   br<u>oo</u>mstick   h<u>oo</u>d   sch<u>oo</u>ner   whirlp<u>oo</u>l   _____

6. **t<u>y</u>pe:**   Nan<u>cy</u>   so<u>y</u>   st<u>y</u>   s<u>y</u>stem   _____

7. **h<u>ea</u>dline:**   c<u>ea</u>se   dis<u>ea</u>sed   r<u>ea</u>lize   thr<u>ea</u>t   _____

8. **N<u>ei</u>l:**   n<u>ei</u>ghbor   rec<u>ei</u>pt   sl<u>ei</u>gh   w<u>ei</u>ght   _____

9. **d<u>ou</u>bt:**   sh<u>ou</u>ld   s<u>ou</u>l   surr<u>ou</u>nd   t<u>ou</u>gh   _____

10. **n<u>ie</u>ce:**   cr<u>ie</u>d   fr<u>ie</u>nd   pl<u>ie</u>rs   shr<u>ie</u>k   _____

6 **Common Ways of Saying Something.** Choose the word at the left that best describes how Americans tend to express themselves in the following cases.

backfired
bounces
bush
catchy
character
cooped
disgrace
fuse
fuss
gab
Greek
jackpot
sink
swear
tone

1. How you describe a person who always seems to be losing his temper: "He has a short _____."

2. How you describe someone who seems quite different from how you expect people to be: "He's a real _____."

3. How you describe someone who talks a lot: "He has the gift of _____."

4. How you describe someone who's just gotten a great deal of money: "He's hit the _____."

5. How you describe something that's gone completely wrong: "My plans _____ on me."

6. What you say to someone who's talking and not really saying anything: "Don't beat around the _____."

7. What you say when you see someone you think you know: "I could _____ that I've met you before."

8. What your mother and father often say when the kids haven't behaved properly: "You're a _____ to this family."

9. What you've often said or heard in an argument: "Watch the _____ of your voice."

10. When a guest asks you what you put in your vegetable soup: "Everything but the kitchen _____."

11. When you can't see why others are so upset: "What's all the _____ about?"

12. When you don't understand something: "It's _____ to me."

13. When you give a reason for wanting to go out a lot: "I just can't stand being _____ up."

14. When you hum or whistle the same song over and over: "That's a _____ tune."

15. When you're disappointed about something that has gone completely wrong: "That's the way the ball _____."

Word Index: Lessons 1-12

A
ain't
airtight
alongside
aloud
ankle
annoy
antonym
apiece
applaud
applause
appoint
appointment
argue
argument
arise
arose
arrest
author
avenue

B
Bacchus
backward
ban
barbecue
bathmat
bathrobe
battered
beech
beyond
bile
birthplace
birthstone
blab
blare
blankly
blaze
blessed
blimp
bloodhound
blond(e)
bloodshed
blowtorch
blubber
blueberry
blur
boastful
bonnet
boost
bother
bout
boyfriend
Braille, L.
brat
breach
breadbox
brighten

brim
brittle
brood
broomstick
broth
brother-in-law
brushoff
budge
budget
burnt
buttermilk
butterscotch

C
cabin
cabinet
calf
capital
capitalize
carefully
carelessly
carfare
Carl
carload
carrot
carton
cartoon
cask
casket
castor oil
catchy
category
cautiously
cease
ceasefire
ceaseless
chairman
champ
chant
chap
chapel
character
charcoal
check-out
cheekbone
cherry
Chicago
childish
chock
chooser
Chris
christen
Christ-like
Christopher
chuck
chuckle
Cincinnati
cinnamon

cite
citizen
citizenship
clack
clamp
clause
cleanse
cleanser
cleat
clinch
cling
clink
clog
closely
clot
clove
clover
clump
coffeepot
coffin
coldly
Colorado
colorblind
Columbus
compact
company
contest
coon
coop
core
cotton
cottonmouth
craft
cram
crank
creak
creaky
creed
creek
crest
cripple
croak
crossbar
crossroad
cruel
Cuba
cucumber
cuddle
cue
cuss
custard

D
damage
darkness
day-care
daylight
daze

deathly
deceased
decent
decently
decision
decoy
deeply
dejected
Denver
depression
dirt-cheap
disable
disappoint
disaster
disclose
discomfort
discount
discussion
diseased
disgrace
disgraceful
disgracefully
disobey
disorderly
disperse
doom
dorm
doubt
doubtful
draft
drawbridge
drawstring
dredge
drifter
drive-in
droop
dropout
druggist
drunken

E
eager
earnings
earthquake
ease
eastern
easygoing
effort
eggplant
Elizabeth
employ
employee
engine
engineer
enlarge
envelope
equal
equally

evil
excitement
explosion
export
eyebrow

F
feature
feedback
fellow
fern
first aid
first-rate
flabby
flatly
flatter
flattery
flex
flick
Florida
floss
flown
flung
foam
follow
follower
footpath
fore
forecast
forehead
forever
fountain
fraction
frail
fraud
Fred
free-for-all
freehand
Frenchman
fret
friendless
frightful
fringe
fro
frost
frostbite
frosting
fruitful
fruity
fussbudget
fuzz

G
gab
gabby
gallbladder
galoshes
gamble

gambler
gap
gape
gargle
gash
gasp
gee-whiz
Genesis
Georgia
gerbil
ghost
gifted
gift-wrap
gig
giggle
gingerly
gingersnap
glassful
glaze
Glen
glider
glittery
glob
glory
glum
goad
goat
goggles
golf
good-bye
good night
granddaughter
grandpa
grandson
grandstand
grant
grasp
grate
grateful
Greenland
greyhound
grim
groin
groove
grope
grubby
gunshot
gush

H
hag
hailstorm
half-wit
Halloween
hardworking
haste
haze

hazy
headlight
headline
head-on
headway
heal
heavyset
he's
highly
hitch
hoax
hoot
horseshoe
host
hotly
hound
humid
humor
humorous
hutch

I
impact
impatience
impossible
incision
incite
indecent
inner
insane
insult
insurance
insure
intelligent
intensely
interest
interesting
investment
invitation
ironmaster
issue

J
jag
jagged
jellybean
jersey
jewel
jeweler
jig
jiggle
Jimmy
joyfully

K
keen
keenly
kindly

L
lain
lawsuit
lease
license
lightheaded
lion
livestock
loafer
loan shark
loin
loop
loophole
loot
looter
Los Angeles
loudmouth
Louis

M
madam
madhouse
Maine
manage
mane
mare
marker
market
marketplace
Mars
marsh
marshmallow
marshy
master
mayonnaise
meantime
member
mercy
Midas
mill
miscall
mister
mixed
moneybags
moreover
moth
mothball
mount
mouthpiece
mustard
mutt

N
Nancy
necessary
necklace
Neil

New Jersey
niece
nightmare
Nile
northeastern
northern
nosebleed
nutmeg

O
obey
odds
oily
ointment
Olson
opening
opportunity
orderly
outburst
outcry
outdoor
outlaw
overjoyed
overpaid

P
package
palace
Pan
panhandle
panhandler
Paris
parson
partner
pastime
patience
payroll
peak
peddler
pencil
per cent
perfect
perfume
permit
perspire
petal
pickup
placement
plainclothes
planter
playmate
playpen
pleasure
pliers
plop
pluck
plumber

poise
poisoner
poisonous
pore
porter
pose
possible
post
postcard
postman
potholder
potpie
power
powerhouse
prank
precise
predict
prepare
prescribe
pressure
prevent
preview
prime
princess
prison
prod
producer
project
prowl
prowler
pullover
puppy
purple

Q
quiz

R
ranch
rancher
rap
reaction
ready-made
ready-to-wear
realize
rebirth
reborn
receipt
recent
recite
recline
recorder
reed
regret
reload
reminder
reorder

replace
replacement
repress
restrain
reverse
review
revolve
revolver
reward
rind
roadside
roam
roomful
roomy
roost
rooster
root
ruby

S
safety
saint
saintly
salute
scab
scalp
scarce
scarcely
schoolhouse
schoolroom
schoolteacher
schooner
Scotland
scramble
scrapbook
scrawl
screwball
scribble
Scripture
scum
self-pity
sh!
shabby
shall
shed
shipshape
shirk
shiver
shoe
shoelace
shoestring
shoplifting
shortchange
showroom
shriek
shrine
shrivel

shrubbery
shrunken
shudder
sickness
silver
silverware
sister-in-law
sketchbook
sketchy
skillet
skim
skimp
skit
slack
slash
slate
slime
slimy
slingshot
slit
slope
slosh
slug
slur
smallpox
smelly
smirk
smock
smother
smuggle
smuggler
snack bar
snare
snazzy
snipe
sniper
snitch
snowflake
snowy
snuff
solo
somewhere
sorehead
soul
southern
southwestern
soy
spar
spareribs
sparkle
spearmint
speedway
spellbound
spike
splashdown
splashy

splatter
splendid
splendidly
splotch
splutter
spotted
sprang
sprig
springtime
sprinkle
spruce
sprung
spun
spur
spy
squad
squash
squawk
squeamish
squid
stab
stack
stag
stagger
steady
steeple
stench
stern
stiff
stock
stole
stolen
stoplight

storybook
straightforward
strangle

strangler
strengthen
strep
stretcher
stride

strikeout
stringy
strive
strut
stub
sty
stylus
suggest

suggestion
supper
surfer
surround
Susan
swank
sway
sweat shirt

swelling
swimsuit
switchblade
swollen
swore
synonym
system

T
tangle
tango
taut

taxi
tempt
thank you
thatched
thee
theirs
theme
thereabout
thereafter
they'd
they'll
thickness

thigh
thirteenth
thorough
thoroughly
thrash
thresh
thresher
thriller
throttle

throwaway
thrust
thruway
ticket
tinkle
toad
tobacco

toilet
toll
tollbooth
torch
totally
tract
trade-in
train wreck
traitor
treason
treasure
treatment
treaty
trench
trespass
trespasser
troublesome
turnpike
twang
tweed
tweezers
twentieth
twig
twirl
twitch
type

U
unaffected
unemployed
unequal
uniform

unlighted
unlock
unnecessary
unsteady
unsuccessful
unsuited
urge
urgent
urgently

V
vain
value
vast
vat
velvet
vent
vet
veteran
veterinarian

W
wail
ware
warehouse
Washington, D.C.
weakness
wealthy
welcome
well-to-do
wept
western
we've
wheelchair

whereabouts
whiner
whiplash
whirlpool
whisper
whistle
White House
whop
whopper
wick
wildfire
willingness
wishbone
wishy-washy
wit
withdraw
woodchuck
wooden
workman
wrestle
wrestler

X

Y
yeast
yoke
yours
youth

Z
zebra
zigzag

Lesson 13

The Letter *y*

In these words, the **y** sounds like a long **i** as in *why*, *rhyme,* and *stylus.*

bye	dye	plywood	cycle	typewriter
bye-bye	lye	style	recycle	typewritten
bypass	rye	nylon	cyclone	typist
bystander	ply		Pyrex	

In these words, the **y** sounds like a short **i** as in *Egypt*, *system,* and *synonym.*

gym	gyp	hymn	mystery	tricycle
gymnasium	gypsy	hymnbook	symptom	

In these words, the **ey** sounds like a long **e** as in *money*, *monkey,* and *whiskey.*

hockey	pulley	valley	volley	volleyball

---

1   **Word Meanings.** Use the words at the left to fill in the blanks.

cyclone
dye
gyp
hymn
lynch
plywood
pulley
Pyrex
recycle
rye
symptom
valley

_____ 1. a grain used in making flour or whiskey

_____ 2. a long lowland between ranges of mountains or other uplands, often having a river or stream running through it

_____ 3. a sign of something

_____ 4. a song of praise or thanksgiving to God; any song of praise or joy

_____ 5. a simple machine for lifting weights made up of a wheel with a grooved rim through which a rope or chain is run

_____ 6. a type of glass that won't melt or crack if exposed to heat

_____ 7. a storm with very strong winds found in the Midwest

_____ 8. thin layers of wood glued tightly together

_____ 9. to cheat someone

_____ 10. to color a piece of cloth by soaking it in a liquid

_____ 11. to hang someone without due process of law

_____ 12. to put through a cycle again for further treatment

Words for Study

Aesop	otherwise	boldness	coward
fables	difficult	solve	crept
moral	chattered	hollow	A.D.
vultures	wealth	elsewhere	intelligence

Aesop and His Fables

Aesop lived in Greece about six hundred years before the birth of Jesus. Not much is known about his life, but it is reported that he was a slave who was given his freedom by his master. The fables that are said to have been written by Aesop were passed along by word of mouth for a long time before people decided to write them down.

A fable is a very short story in which a lesson or a moral is given to us about how we act or should act. Even though many of these fables seem to be stories about animals, they are really stories about human beings.

Here are a few of Aesop's fables.

The Fox and the Goat

One day a fox was nosing around a well. By accident, his foot slipped on a wet stone and he fell in. The water wasn't deep, but the well was. Though the fox tried and tried, he could not get out of the well.

"What are you doing down there?" he heard someone ask.

Upon looking up, the fox saw a goat peering at him. Quickly, the fox replied, "Enjoying myself! They say there will be no rain for a long time, and all the wells will go dry. I am drinking my fill, so I won't die and be left for the vultures to feed on. Come on down—the water's fine!"

The foolish goat didn't stop to think but jumped right down into the well. The fox, of course, wanted to use him to get out of the well. He leaped at once on the goat's back, set one foot on his horns, and jumped out of the well.

As the fox left, he called out to the poor goat, "You're a silly goat, my friend. Otherwise, you would have looked before you leaped!"

Moral: Think how you will get yourself out of a difficult spot before you get yourself into one.

The Goose That Laid the Golden Eggs

A farmer had a gray goose which gave him a big surprise one day. In her nest, he found a strange egg which was as yellow as gold and very heavy. At first, the farmer was certain someone had played a trick on him. Then he realized that the egg was real gold.

"Wife!" he chattered happily as soon as he got in the house. "See what our gray goose has laid—an egg of real gold!"

The next day the farmer found another golden egg in the nest. And the next day he found another. It was wonderful! But by this time, the farmer had grown greedy for more and more wealth. "Why should I wait?" he thought. "If I cut the goose open, I shall get all her golden eggs at once. I will have great wealth in a minute!"

So, with great boldness, the farmer killed the goose, but found not a single egg inside. And his good gray goose was dead.

Moral: People who are greedy often throw away what they already have.

The Old Lion and the Fox

A lion grew so old that he could no longer hunt for his food. But old or not, he had to eat, so he thought of a scheme to solve his problem. He would pretend he was sick. Then, when any animals came to visit, he would eat them up.

The lion's scheme worked out just as he had planned. He lay down near the mouth of his cave and began to groan. One after another, the beasts came to ask him what was the matter. The lion invited them in, and that was the end of them.

One day, the fox heard the lion groaning. He came up and sat down in the hollow of an old tree outside the lion's cave. "Aren't you feeling well?" he inquired.

"I am very ill, my friend," the lion replied. "It is so lonely lying here by myself all day. Do come in and visit me for a little while."

"Well, I'd like to," responded the fox. "But I see by the tracks that you've had quite a lot of animals visiting you lately. I also see that the tracks go only one way. Until the animals that have gone into your cave come out again, I think I shall visit friends elsewhere."

Moral: Be warned by what happens to others.

The Monkey and the Cat

A monkey and a cat were pets in the same house. They were good friends and were always doing something naughty together. One day they were sitting in front of a fire, watching some chestnuts roasting.

"How nice it would be to have some chestnuts," the monkey sighed. "You're no coward like me, Kitty. You are so brave. Pull some chestnuts out of the fire, and we shall have ourselves a fine treat."

Now the cat didn't want to put her paw so close to the flames, but she was flattered by what the monkey had said about her. So she crept carefully right up to the fire and, just as carefully, drew out a chestnut with her paw. Even though she burned her paw each time, she did this again and again. As fast as she pulled the chestnuts out of the fire, the monkey gobbled them up.

At last, the cat could stand the pain no longer, and she sat down to lick her paw. Glaring at the monkey, she said, "Next time, I'll know better. I'll never pull chestnuts out of the fire for you again."

Moral: Watch out! The person who flatters you always wants to get something out of you.

Adapted from *Aesop's Fables*, retold by Anne Terry White. Copyright © 1964 by Anne Terry White. Reprinted by permission of Random House, Inc.

2 **About the Fables.** Complete each statement with the right answer.

1. Aesop was _____.
   (a) English   (c) German
   (b) French   (d) Greek

2. The letters that stand for the time that Aesop lived are _____
   (a) A.D.   (c) B.C.
   (b) A.M.   (d) P.M.

3. At first, people knew about the fables from _____.
   (a) notebooks
   (b) other people telling them
   (c) radio
   (d) scrolls

4. A moral is _____.
   (a) a lesson
   (b) a story
   (c) an idea
   (d) the last sentence

5. The advice that the goat in the first fable should have taken is: _____

   _____
   (a) Don't go near the water.
   (b) Haste makes waste.
   (c) Look before you leap.
   (d) We don't know the worth of water until the well is dry.

6. Which saying best expresses the meaning of the moral of the second fable? _____

   _____
   (a) A bird in the hand is worth two in the bush.
   (b) All that glitters is not gold.
   (c) Early to bed and early to rise makes a man healthy, wealthy, and wise.
   (d) Money is the root of all evil.

7. Based on your reading of these four fables, the wisest animal in a fable is often _____.
   (a) a fox
   (b) a goat
   (c) a lion
   (d) a monkey

8. Based on your reading of these fables, which of these traits do you think Aesop regarded as the most

   important? _____
   (a) beauty
   (b) health
   (c) intelligence
   (d) kindness

3 **Write Your Own Moral.** Read the following fable. Then write a moral for it.

The Grasshopper and the Ant

All summer long the grasshopper could be heard singing in the fields. As he hopped and leaped, he sang away at the top of his voice, "The leaves taste so good! It is so nice to be alive!"

The summer days passed quickly, and it seemed to the grasshopper that he barely turned around when already it was fall. The cold wind was blowing, all the flowers and grasses in the field were dead, and there was nothing to eat.

"Please," said the grasshopper, limping over to an ant, "will you give me something to eat?"

The ant was busy dragging a dead fly into the nest. It was one of a hundred insects she had lugged home, for she had worked hard all summer long to store up enough food for the winter.

"Something to eat?" asked the ant in a stern voice. "All you did was sing and prance all summer. Well, my good fellow, now let's see you dance!"

Moral: _____

4 **Adding -y to a Word.** Study the spelling examples. Then, add -y to the words listed below.

1. dress _dressy_   1. haze _hazy_   1. gab _gabby_

2. lump _____   2. lace _____   2. fur _____

3. fuzz _____   3. slime _____   3. bag _____

4. foam _____   4. spine _____   4. spot _____

5. silver _____   5. groove _____   5. wit _____

5 **More Common Ways of Speaking.** Use the words at the left to complete these common American expressions.

ape
butterflies
camels
flea
frog
gnats
goat
goose
horses
lion's
lobster
monkey
mouse
puppy
shark
shrimp

1. In describing a coward, it's often said, "He's so scared, he couldn't hurt

   a _____."

2. When a person's skin is burned badly by the sun, he's "as red as

   a _____."

3. When someone makes you really angry, he "gets your _____."

4. When you destroy somebody's chances, you "cook his _____."

5. When you have stage fright, it feels as if there are "_____ in your stomach."

6. When you help yourself to the biggest part of something, you take "the

   _____ share."

7. When you play or fiddle around with something, you "_____ with it."

8. When you think someone is acting like a coward, you ask, "Are you a man or

   a _____?"

9. When young teenagers fall in love, adults often call this "_____ love."

10. When you need to clear your throat, you have "a _____ in your throat."

11. This slang term is used to describe a person who lends you money at extremely

    high interest rates: loan _____.

12. This slang term is used to describe someone who is short: _____.

13. To copy something that someone else has done is to "_____" him.

14. To restrain yourself from doing something is to "hold your _____."

15. This is what Jesus had to say about people who make a big deal out of little issues and don't regard the really big issues in life as important: "They strain

    at _____ and swallow _____."

6 **Compound Words.** Choose a word from **List A** and add a word from **List B** to fill in the blanks.

List A	List B
apple	age
bed	box
chatter	broken
drive	cases
edge	chair
head	dog
house	pen
high	phones
nit	room
pig	sauce
pillow	song
play	stepped
side	sty
sing	way
teen	wise
watch	wit

1. As William carefully _____ the mess on the living room rug, he roared, "If that mutt isn't _____ by Friday, he's going straight to the pound!"

2. "But, Daddy," the children cried sweetly in their _____ voices, "you just said yesterday—when he scared off that prowler—that our puppy will be a first-rate _____."

3. "My goodness," exclaimed Aunt Ruth upon entering her niece's _____. "I came here to get away from the farm, and here I am—right back in a _____."

4. While scrubbing the _____, Scott wondered if his one-year-old son was mistaking the kitchen for a _____ rather than a place to eat.

5. When Lynn complained to her sister-in-law that no one ever told her anything, her sister-in-law replied, "Well, you're such a _____, that nobody can ever get a word in _____."

6. Christopher, who was convinced that his sister was a total _____, said in disgust, "Of course the radio doesn't sound great—you're not using the _____."

7. After backing her car into the _____, Ms. Porter dashed into the kitchen to get the _____ cake she had baked for the October Fair only to discover that half of it had been eaten.

8. On Christmas morning, Mother burst into tears when she unwrapped the sheets and _____ her _____ daughters had given her and exclaimed, "Why don't I ever get something that's just for me—like flowers or perfume or a pretty blouse!"

Lesson 14

Double Consonants in the Middle of Words

To help sound out these words, draw a line between the double consonants and sound out the words using the rules you have studied. In most cases, the first vowel is short.

ladder	sissy	mellow	kettle	correct
litter	dizzy	shallow	rattle	comma
differ	grizzly	sparrow	riddle	lettuce
trigger	mummy	arrow	puddle	Kenneth
slugger	tummy	sorrow	puzzle	gossip
soccer	petty		wiggle	
error	button	puppet	mattress	
terror	ribbon	parrot	goddess	
horror	kitten	rabbit	address	

1 **Word Meanings.**

A. Match the synonyms.

differ
dizzy
error
litter
petty
riddle
sissy
slugger
sorrow
terror
tummy
wiggle

_____ 1. coward

_____ 2. disagree

_____ 3. fear

_____ 4. fighter

_____ 5. lightheaded

_____ 6. mistake

_____ 7. puzzle

_____ 8. sadness

_____ 9. squirm

_____ 10. stomach

_____ 11. trash

_____ 12. unimportant

B. Match the antonyms.

correct
differ
goddess   _____   1. agree
littered
mellow   _____   2. clean
petty   _____   3. clear
puzzling
shallow   _____   4. deep
sissy
sorrow   _____   5. god
terror
wiggly   _____   6. hero

_____   7. important

_____   8. incorrect

_____   9. joy

_____   10. peace or calm

_____   11. still

_____   12. tense or harsh

Words for Study

Margaret	clatter	fumbling	bleachers
Lucy	hawk-nosed	pricked	usher
gaily	footsteps	Arizona	sculpture

The Terror in the Streets

The boys in the streets reminded her of tough gangs in the movies, and the apartment building was shabby, but Margaret was tired of looking for a place to live. She took the apartment.

She was afraid from the day she moved in, but she hung several paintings and tried to think of the place as home. Still she remained uneasy. The dirty buildings and the gloomy streets bothered her more each day. "Now my life," she thought, "is mostly fear."

It was the age of the groups on the street late at night that made her most uneasy. The boys stood by the all-night hamburger shop just outside the subway station on Sixth Avenue. They could not be more than sixteen or seventeen, and some seemed even younger. One boy really scared her. He stood out so because of his color. His skin looked light green to her.

The boys seemed to do nothing but wait. What they were waiting for was not clear. Their eyes followed her when she went into the subway station to go uptown, and their eyes were still there waiting when she returned.

She was afraid at night, and she felt she could not trust the bolt on the door. But Mr. T., whom she brought up to look at it, wouldn't listen to her. "Why that a good bolt," he said. "You no be afraid with that bolt. I fix it myself." What would she do, she wondered, if somebody did break in? Surely no one would ever hear her; no one would find her for days.

The green-faced boy seemed to watch her from the first day. But it was some time during her second week there that he began to speak to her. It was always the same word—she didn't understand it at first.

"Hey, Lucy."

She'd made it out at last. Her first idea was that he'd said "juicy", which confused her. But "Lucy" was just as puzzling.

At home she would stop working in the afternoon and lie on the bed, thinking of him and of the sneaky little gang always grouped around him. "Is he always there?" she wondered. "Doesn't he have a home?"

On Saturday night, Margaret went to a party. She had six drinks and, during a pause in the talking, she heard herself say, "I wonder if the rest of you feel as I do about the streets these days?" She knew she had had too much to drink, but she couldn't stop herself. "I mean the terror in the streets . . . Aren't any of you afraid to go out?" Her heart began pounding. She knew that everyone in the room was staring at her, but she did not try to hold back. "I really can't see how you can talk so gaily about life when life is like it is."

She got up. She had said almost nothing all evening, and now she was talking like this. "I think I'd better go." And she walked out, not really caring what they thought about her.

On her way home, she decided to stop at the all-night hamburger shop for a cup of coffee. She did not even glance at the boys as she passed them. She had just put down the money when the boys from outside came in. Her heart almost stopped—there were empty seats around her and they were taking them.

She put the cup down with a clatter. He was on her right, and he was looking at her, the green hawk-nosed boy. But he wouldn't speak.

She got up and hurried out on the street. "Hey!"

She glanced over her shoulder to see him in the doorway, and she began to run . . . footsteps behind her . . . coming faster. She kept running, up the four flights of stairs, down the hall to her own door.

Fumbling with the lock, she heard him coming. She got it open and ran in and threw the bolt. Then she went back into the bedroom to check the window lock. She had just returned to the kitchen to turn off the light when the rap came. She began to shake, each hair on her head pricked into her scalp.

Tap-tap-tap.

Even when she heard his footsteps going away, she was unable to move. At last she sat down on a chair. She felt that she had come within an inch of dying and had escaped. She would have to get away. Tomorrow she would sell all her things and buy a ticket back to Arizona.

She woke up with the sun shining in her eyes. For a long while she didn't move, but lay there thinking about last night: "It is almost as if I went there to tempt him to follow me," she thought. The idea seemed so close to the truth that it frightened her.

She got up and went into the kitchen. "My bag!" She knew she had left it on the counter when she'd fled from the hamburger shop. Well, it didn't matter. She must hurry if she was going to make plans for moving.

She had some trouble withdrawing the bolt, but after a few minutes it worked. She opened the door and stood there, not believing what she saw.

Swinging by its strap from the outside door-knob was her cheap leather bag, as real as her most awful fears. She grabbed it up in both hands, slammed the door shut, and began to cry in a way that she had never cried before. She could not take her eyes off the handbag—this message about the kind of person she was that the world had left at her door.

Adapted with permission of the author, Robert Lowry.

2 **About the Story.** Put the letter of the best answer on the line.

_____ 1. Margaret is frightened _____.

(a) by her landlord
(b) from the very beginning
(c) when she sees the strange boy
(d) when she drinks too much

_____ 2. The thing that frightens Margaret most about the boys who hang out on the corner is their _____.

(a) age
(b) race
(c) size
(d) swearing

_____ 3. Why does the boy call Margaret "Lucy"?

(a) She reminds him of his mother.
(b) He knows this annoys her.
(c) He thinks this is her name.
(d) The author doesn't offer a reason.

_____ 4. We can guess from the way that Mr. T. speaks that he _____.

(a) does not know how to repair locks
(b) is not a very concerned landlord
(c) thinks Margaret is crazy
(d) was most likely born in another country

_____ 5. Based on the story, Margaret normally uses _____ to get around.

    (a) automobiles   (c) taxis

    (b) buses   (d) the subway

_____ 6. Margaret acts the way she does at the party because _____.

    (a) she doesn't care what others think of her

    (b) she doesn't know the other guests very well

    (c) she has really let fear rule her life

    (d) she wants to insult the host

_____ 7. Margaret understands that the reason she probably went to the coffee shop was that _____.

    (a) she wanted to become friends with the green-faced boy

    (b) she wanted to tempt the green-faced boy

    (c) she was afraid to go home

    (d) she was too drunk to go home

_____ 8. When Margaret sees that her handbag is missing, _____.

    (a) she calls the police

    (b) she decides to go back to Arizona

    (c) she doesn't really care

    (d) she knows who has stolen it

_____ 9. The green-faced boy most likely _____.

    (a) cares about Margaret

    (b) is a mugger

    (c) thinks Margaret is a snob

    (d) wants to harm Margaret

_____ 10. This story probably takes place in _____.

    (a) a small town   (c) the country

    (b) the city   (d) the West

3   **What Do You Think?** Read the ending of the story again before answering these questions in good sentence form.

1. Why do you think Margaret cries so hard when she sees her handbag on the doorknob?

_____

_____

2. An American president once said, "We have nothing to fear but fear itself." Think about Margaret in this story and explain what this quote means.

_____

_____

_____

4 **The City.** Put the words at the left into the correct categories. Use each word only once.

bartenders	paintings
bleachers	previews
cocktails	scoreboard
drawings	screen
goal posts	sculpture
guards	tickets
jazz	ushers
locker rooms	waitresses

Movies

1. _____
2. _____
3. _____
4. _____

Nightclubs

1. _____
2. _____
3. _____
4. _____

Museums

1. _____
2. _____
3. _____
4. _____

Stadiums

1. _____
2. _____
3. _____
4. _____

5 **The Ending -*ment*.** Use the words at the left to fill in the blanks.

argument
appointment
department
disappointment
excitement
improvement
installment
pavement
payments
refreshment

1. When people who have grown up in the country come to the city, they are

   often in for a big _____.

2. Their first shock is seeing that there is much more _____ than there is grass.

3. Their second shock is finding out how much they have to pay for sodas and hot

   dogs at the _____ stands.

4. Still another shock is watching how everybody seems to be hurrying off

   somewhere as if they're late for an _____.

5. It costs so much to live in a city that most people have to buy items on the

   _____ plan.

6. They reason that by making monthly _____ on such items as
   stoves, TV's, etc., they can own more.

7. Owing money, they argue, is an _____ upon owning nothing
   at all.

8. This _____ may seem to make sense, but many people spend
   a great deal of time worrying about how they're going to pay their monthly bills.

9. The _____ stores don't help this matter any, for their
   windows are always filled with tempting goods.

10. Nevertheless, for many people, the _____ that a city offers is
    well worth the price of all the hurrying and worrying.

Lesson 15

Two Consonants in the Middle of Words

Even though these words do not have double consonants in the middle, you still draw a line between the two middle consonants to sound out the word. In most cases, the first vowel is short.

platform	walrus	mental	signal	Vermont
napkin	pardon	pester	sponsor	organ
admire	target	ignore	lumber	survive
ambush	darling	ignite	trumpet	curfew
walnut	tender	witness	sermon	powder

1 Word Meanings.

A. Match the synonyms.

admire
advance
darling
ignite
pardon
pester
rescue
seldom
target
witness

_____	1. annoy
_____	2. excuse
_____	3. goal
_____	4. light
_____	5. move forward
_____	6. rarely
_____	7. respect
_____	8. save
_____	9. see
_____	10. sweetheart

B. Match the antonyms.

admired
advance
ignite
ignore
pardon
pester
seldom
survived
tender
unseen

_____	1. blame
_____	2. died
_____	3. ignore
_____	4. listen to
_____	5. often
_____	6. put out
_____	7. disliked
_____	8. retreat
_____	9. tough
_____	10. witnessed

Words for Study

Memphis	grocery	yanked	parents
mama	briskly	stark	refer
where's	overtook	scattered	dictionary

The Streets of Memphis

Hunger stole upon me so slowly that at first I was not aware of what hunger really meant. The hunger I had known before this had been a normal hunger, but this new hunger scared me and made me angry. For the first time in my life I had to pause and think of what was happening to me.

"Mama, I'm hungry," I complained one afternoon.

"You'll have to wait," she told me. "There's nothing to eat."

"But I'm hungry!"

She was ironing and she paused and looked at me with tears in her eyes. "Where's your father?" she asked me.

I stared at her. Yes, it was true that my father had not come home to sleep for many days now and I could make as much noise as I wanted. I had not known why he wasn't there, but I was glad that he was not there to shout his rules at me. It had never crossed my mind, however, that his not being there would mean no food.

My mother went to work as a cook and left me and my brother alone in the flat each day with a loaf of bread and a pot of tea. When she returned at evening, she would be tired and depressed and would cry a lot. Whenever we asked why father had left, she would tell us that we were too young to know.

One evening my mother told me that I would have to do the shopping for food. I was proud; I felt like a grownup. The next afternoon I looped the basket over my arm and went down the street toward the store. When I reached the corner, a gang of boys grabbed me, knocked me down, snatched the basket, took the money, and sent me running home in fear. That evening I told my mother what had happened, but she made no comment. She sat down at once, wrote another note, gave me more money, and sent me out to the grocery again. I crept down the steps and saw the same gang of boys playing down the street. I ran back into the house.

"What's the matter?" my mother asked.

"It's those same boys," I said. "They'll beat me."

"You've got to get over that," she said. "Now go on."

I went out of the door and walked briskly down the sidewalk, praying that the gang would not beat me up. But when I came near them, someone shouted.

"There he is!"

They came toward me and I broke into a wild run toward home. They overtook me and flung me down. I yelled, pleaded, and kicked, but they wrenched the money out of my hand. They yanked me to my feet, gave me a few slaps and sent me home sobbing. My mother met me at the door.

"You just stay right where you are," she said in a deadly tone. "I'm going to teach you this night to stand up and fight for yourself."

I was confused. My mother was telling me to fight, a thing that she had never done before. "But I'm scared," I said.

"Go now!" she said as she handed me more money, another note and a long heavy stick. "If you come back into this house without those groceries, I'll whip you!"

She slammed the door and I heard the key turn in the lock. I shook with fright. I had the choice of being beaten at home or away from home. I clutched the stick, crying, trying to reason. If I were beaten in the streets, I had a chance to fight and defend myself. I walked slowly down the sidewalk, coming closer to the gang of boys, holding the stick tightly. I was so full of fear that I could scarcely breathe.

"There he is again!" the cry went up. They surrounded me quickly and began to grab for my hand.

"I'll kill you!" I threatened.

They closed in. In blind fear I let the stick fly, feeling it crack against a boy's skull. I fought to knock them cold, to kill them so that they could not strike back at me. I struck with tears in my eyes, teeth clenched, stark fear making me throw every ounce of my strength behind each blow. I hit again and again, dropping the money and the grocery list. The boys scattered.

I stood panting, egging them on, daring them to come on and fight. When they refused, I ran after them and they tore out for their homes, screaming. The parents of the boys rushed into the streets and threatened me, and for the first time in my life I shouted at grownups, telling them that I would give them the same if they got in my way. I found my grocery list and the money and went to the store. On my way back I kept my stick ready for use, but there was not a single boy in sight. That night I won the right to the streets of Memphis.

---

2 **About the Story.** Answer these questions in good sentence form. Be sure to explain your answers.

1. Why do you think it takes so long for the boy to see that his father has left home?

_____

_____

2. Why do you think that the mother insists that her son does the grocery shopping?

_____

_____

3. What do you think of the way in which the mother handles her son?

_____

_____

4. If the story had continued, describe how you think the boy would have acted after winning the fight with the gang.

_____

_____

_____

5. How is the gang in this story different from the gang in "The Terror in the Streets"?

_____

_____

_____

3 **More Work with Synonyms.** Choose the synonym for the first word in each line and write it to the right. Study the example before you begin.

1. **ray:**	beam	groove	noon	sunlight	*beam*
2. **peak:**	bottom	mountain	slope	top	_____
3. **consumer:**	buyer	citizen	seller	cheapskate	_____
4. **greedy:**	wealthy	selfish	friendless	hardworking	_____
5. **immense:**	compact	ideal	overgrown	vast	_____
6. **brisk:**	budge	creepy	staggering	fast	_____
7. **concept:**	feeling	idea	program	sense	_____
8. **disperse:**	pardon	pester	rescue	scatter	_____
9. **gyp:**	cheat	clinch	pressure	thrash	_____
10. **stark:**	stormy	petty	doubtful	bare	_____
11. **symptom:**	cause	cycle	pain	sign	_____
12. **moral:**	style	mystery	lesson	expression	_____

4 **The Ending -ness.** Sound out the words at the left. Then use these words to fill in the blanks.

brightness
carelessness
closeness
fitness
illness
shyness
tenderness
thoughtfulness
thoughtlessness
willingness

1. The _____ of the two front runners made reporters unwilling to predict who the winner would be.

2. Elizabeth felt such _____ toward people in pain that she decided to go to nursing school in September.

3. Experts tell us that the main cause of accidents is _____

4. Glen missed three months of work because of his _____

5. Have you ever met a person who tries to hide his _____ by bragging a lot about how great he is?

6. Jerome had to pass a _____ test to get in the army.

7. Linda's _____ always made her friends wonder why they liked her in the first place.

8. Mary's _____ always cheered up her friends.

9. The _____ of the sun blinded Jack, who had been exploring a cave all morning and afternoon.

10. Bobby defined success as a _____ to go above and beyond the call of duty no matter how tired or upset he felt.

5 **Changing y to i.** In the following words, the _y_ is changed to _i_ before -_ness_ is added. Study the example and then add -_ness_ to these words.

1. friendly   _friendliness_

2. sloppy   _____

3. heavy   _____

4. empty   _____

5. fussy   _____

6. greedy   _____

7. lumpy   _____

8. roomy   _____

9. steady   _____

10. fuzzy   _____

11. sticky   _____

12. grouchy   _____

13. slimy   _____

14. hazy   _____

15. costly   _____

16. petty   _____

6 **American Cities.** Match the states listed at the left with the cities. Use the rules you've learned for sounding out the words you've not yet studied. If you get really stuck, ask a friend or refer to the dictionary.

California
Colorado
Florida
Hawaii
Georgia
Illinois
Maryland
Massachusetts
Michigan
New Jersey
New York
Ohio
Tennessee
Texas
Washington

1. Atlanta is in the state of _____.

2. Atlantic City is in the state of _____.

3. Baltimore is in the state of _____.

4. Boston is in the state of _____.

5. Chicago is in the state of _____.

6. Cleveland is in the state of _____.

7. Denver is in the state of _____.

8. Dallas is in the state of _____.

9. Detroit is in the state of _____.

10. Honolulu is in the state of _____.

11. Los Angeles is in the state of _____.

12. Memphis is in the state of _____.

13. Miami is in the state of _____.

14. New York City is in the state of _____.

15. Seattle is in the state of _____.

Lesson 16

More Work with Two Consonants in the Middle of Words

absent	ransom	parcel	fender	hectic	boycott
banjo	vampire	margin	Edward	obtain	slumber
lantern	shampoo	altar	estate	oblong	turnip
canteen	garlic	alter	census	Moscow	burden
cactus	harness	wisdom	welfare	London	persist

1 **Word Meanings.** Use the words at the left to fill in the blanks.

absent
boycotting
burden
cactus
canteen
census
estate
harness
hectic
London
Moscow
obtain
persist
ransom
slumber
vampire

_____ 1. A heavy load is called a _____.

_____ 2. Another word that means to get something is _____.

_____ 3. If you're not present in a class or at a meeting, you're _____.

_____ 4. In stories, this is a corpse that rises from the grave at night to suck the blood of sleeping persons.

_____ 5. The price or payment demanded for the release of a kidnapped person or property is called _____.

_____ 6. This large piece of land in the country often has a big house on it.

_____ 7. This plant is most often found in the deserts of the New World.

_____ 8. This container for water is used by campers or people in the army.

_____ 9. This is another word for sleep.

_____ 10. This is put on a horse, donkey, etc., in order to pull a plow or cart.

_____ 11. This is taken in the United States every ten years to find out how many people live in the country.

_____ 12. This is the capital city of England.

_____ 13. This is the capital city of Russia.

_____ 14. To keep trying no matter how hard the chore or task may seem is to _____.

_____ 15. When you join with others to stop using something because you are against it or want to force a change, you are _____.

_____ 16. You can use this word to describe a day that seemed very confused and fast to you.

Words for Study

naw	dove	flattened	Stuart
lonesome	tackle	spurted	homonym
haymaker	scooted	handkerchief	factory

The Thread That Runs So True

"Did you forget something, Guy?" I asked.

"Naw, I've never forgot nothin'," he reminded me.

"Then what do you want?" I asked.

"Whip you," he said. "I didn't like your sister. You know what I done to her."

"Yes, I know what you did to her," I said.

"I'm a-goin' to do the same thing to you," he threatened. "I don't like you. I don't like teachers. I said never another person with your name would teach this school. Not as long as I'm here."

"Can you go to another school?" I asked, my temper rising.

"Naw, naw," he shouted, "if anybody leaves, you'll leave. I was in Lonesome Valley first. And I ain't a-goin' to no other school because of you!"

I looked at his face. It was red as a sliced beet. Fire danced in his pale blue eyes. I knew Guy meant every word he said. I knew I had to face him and to fight. There was no other way around.

"Will you let me take my necktie off?" I said, remembering I'd been choked by a fellow pulling my necktie once in a fight.

"Yep, take off that purty tie. Roll up the sleeves of your white shirt too," he said. "But they'll be dirty by the time I sweep this floor up with you."

He shot out his long arm but I ducked. I felt the wind from his thrust against my ear. I mustn't let him clinch me, I thought.

Then he came back with another right and I ducked his second lick. I came around with my first lick—a right—and planted it on his jaw, not a good lick but just enough to jar him and make him madder. When he rushed at me, I sidestepped. He missed. By the time he had turned around, I caught him a haymaker on the chin that reeled him. Then I followed up with another lick as hard as I had ever hit a man. Yet I didn't bring him down. He came back for more. But he didn't reach me this time. He was right. I did get my

shirt dirty. I dove through the air with a flying tackle. I hit him beneath the knees. I'd tackled like this in football. I'd tackled hard. And I never tackled anybody harder than Guy. His feet went from under him, and I scooted past on the pine floor. I'd tackled him so quickly when he expected me to come back at him with my fists, that he went down before he could catch himself with his hands. His face hit flat against the floor and his nose was flattened. The blood spurted as he started to get up.

I let him get to his feet. I wondered if I should. For I knew it was either him or me. One of us had to whip. When he did get to his feet after that awful fall, I waded into him. I hit fast and I hit hard. He swung wild. His fingernail took a streak of hide from my neck and left a red mark that smarted, and the blood oozed through. I pounded his chin. I caught him on the jaw. I reeled him back and followed up. I gave him a left to the short ribs while my right in a split second caught his mouth. Blood spurted again. Yet he was not through. But I knew I had him.

"Had enough?" I panted.

He didn't answer. I didn't ask him a second time. I hit him hard enough to knock two men down. I followed up with a haymaker under the chin and laid him across the desk. Then he rolled to the floor with blood running from his nose and mouth. His eyes were rolled back.

I was nearly out of breath. My hands hurt badly. My heart pounded. "If this is teaching school!" I thought. "If this goes with it!" Then I remembered I had asked for it. I'd asked for this school. I would take no other.

When Guy came to his senses, he looked up at me. I was putting a wet, cool handkerchief on his head. When he started to get up, I helped him to his feet.

"Mr. Stuart, I really got it poured on me," he admitted. "You're some fighter."

This was the first time he had ever called me "Mr. Stuart."

"I'm not much of a fighter until I have to fight, Guy," I said. "You asked for it. There was no way around. I had to fight you."

"I know it," he said. "I've had in mind to whip you ever since I heard you's a-goin' to teach this school. But you win. You winned fair, too," he admitted. "I didn't think you could hit like that."

Guy was still weak. His nose and mouth kept bleeding. He didn't have a handkerchief, and I gave him a clean one.

"Think you can make it home all right, Guy?"

"I think so," he said. He walked slower from the schoolhouse than he had walked in.

---

2 **About the Story.** Complete these sentences with the best answer.

1. Mr. Stuart had to fight Guy because _____

_____.

   (a) Guy refused to settle the matter any other way
   (b) Guy had beaten up his sister
   (c) he did not want to be thought of as a "chicken"
   (d) he knew that Guy deserved to get a beating

2. This fight was important because Mr. Stuart _____

_____.

   (a) earned Guy's respect
   (b) learned to accept Guy's faults
   (c) proved that he was a better fighter than Guy
   (d) showed Guy who was boss

3. Guy shows that he has a sense of what is fair and decent _____

_____.

   (a) when he beat up Mr. Stuart's sister   (c) during the fight with Mr. Stuart
   (b) before the fight with Mr. Stuart   (d) after the fight with Mr. Stuart

4. A main theme expressed in this story is that _____

_____.

   (a) a clean and pretty schoolhouse is important to the students
   (b) it is difficult to reason with a person who has made up his mind to fight you
   (c) it is impossible to teach a group of wild students
   (d) the best way to make students act properly is to beat them up

5. This story probably takes place _____.

   (a) in a boys' reform school   (c) in New York City
   (b) in a country, one-room schoolhouse   (d) two hundred years ago

3 **Putting Details in Order.** Put these details in the order in which they happened by placing the correct number before each detail. Note that the first one has been done for you.

__1__ Guy beats up Mr. Stuart's sister.

_____ Guy's face hits the floor.

_____ Guy's fingernail takes some skin from Mr. Stuart's neck.

_____ Guy misses Mr. Stuart as he rushes him.

_____ Guy rolls to the floor with blood running down his face.

_____ Mr. Stuart asks Guy if he has had enough.

_____ Mr. Stuart tackles Guy.

_____ Mr. Stuart takes a job at Lonesome Valley School.

_____ Mr. Stuart takes his necktie off.

_____ Mr. Stuart wipes Guy's face with his handkerchief.

4 **Can You Help Guy with His English?** Rewrite the following sentences using more formal English.

1. "Naw, I've never forgot nothing."

_____

2. "And I ain't a-goin' to no other school because of you!"

_____

3. "Yep, take off that purty tie too."

_____

4. "You winned fair too."

_____

5 The Endings -*ful* and -*less.* Use the words at the left to fill in the blanks.

Group A

distressful
graceful
meaningful
mindful
rightful
sinful
sorrowful
willful

1. Because Kenneth was not _____ of the time, he was an hour late for his appointment.

2. Jimmy was such a _____ little boy that whenever he didn't get his way, he would throw himself on the floor and scream until his parents gave in.

3. Some actions that were regarded as _____ in former times are now regarded by some people as "no big deal."

4. The judge ordered the thief to restore all the stolen goods to their _____ owners within thirty days.

5. The outfielder made a _____ leap for the ball and then fell into the third row of the bleachers.

6. The stray puppy had such _____ eyes that Steven decided to take her home in spite of the fact that he already had four dogs.

7. When life seems really _____, the best thing to do sometimes is to have a good, long cry.

8. Whenever her father gave her a _____ look, May knew she was about to hear one of his "little talks" about how young ladies should behave.

Group B

ceaseless
errorless
fruitless
hatless
motherless
regardless
senseless
toothless

1. For several moments, Guy lay _____ on the schoolroom floor after his fight with Mr. Stuart.

2. In spite of the fact that the Yankees were playing _____ baseball, they were still trailing by five runs at the seventh inning stretch.

3. In spite of the president's _____ efforts to end the war, the two countries continued to fight.

4. Matthew decided to go to the soccer game _____ of the fact that all the weather reports predicted a heavy afternoon downpour.

5. The baby's _____ grin delighted the family so much that they loved to discover new ways to make him smile.

6. The entire neighborhood was deeply concerned about the fate of the

   _____ children who lived at the end of the block.

7. The president and the treasurer both agreed that the weekly meeting had been

   totally _____ because the group had been unable to agree on anything.

8. When the officer asked the young woman if the mugger had worn a hat, she

   responded, "No, he was _____."

6 **Homonyms.** Homonyms are words that sound the same but have different meanings and spellings. Use each pair of homonyms listed below to complete the sentences correctly.

cellar *and* seller

1. Mrs. North was the most successful _____ at the yard sale that the neighborhood women held in Mrs. West's _____ last weekend.

wears *and* where's

2. "_____ the lady who claims she _____ a size ten dress?" shouted the saleswoman rudely.

gnaw *and* naw

3. When his grandmother asked Brady if he wanted her to save the bones from the roast beef for his dog, he replied, "_____, the vet said it ain't good for dogs to _____ on bones."

heal *and* heel

4. Because the wound on Pearl's _____ wouldn't _____ properly, her mother decided they'd better go to the hospital.

creak *and* creek

5. As the children were fishing down at the _____, they were frightened to hear something _____ behind them.

fore *and* four

6. "_____!" shouted Herb, and the _____ men watched him sink a hole-in-one.

die *and* dye

7. People who work in factories can _____ from having to put their hands in _____ over a long span of time.

grate *and* great

8. Joyce thought there was nothing so _____ on a cold, winter evening as watching the burning coals on the _____.

beach *and* beech

9. The _____ trees at the edge of the _____ gave welcome shade to the sunbathers who were beginning to burn.

real *and* reel

10. It was a _____ shock to Luke when he learned how long it would take him to save for a new fishing rod and _____.

cite *and* sight

11. The president's _____ was so poor that someone had to point out the men whom he was to _____ for their brave conduct during the fire.

lain *and* lane

12. Everyone knew Louis was crazy when they learned he had _____ in the middle of Midas _____ all night, waiting for a car to run him over.

altar *and* alter

13. If the groom had let the tailor _____ the length of his trousers just one more inch, he would have certainly looked more handsome as he stood beside his bride at the _____.

Review: Lessons 1-16

1 **Word Study.** Choose the correct answer at the left and write it on the line.

Aesop
ambush
comma
curfew
fable
gossip
grocery
haymaker
mummy
sissy
slugger
sponsor
turnip
vulture
witness

_____ 1. a business that buys time on radio or TV programs to run ads

_____ 2. a Greek writer of fables who lived about 600 B.C.

_____ 3. a large bird that often feeds on dead animals

_____ 4. a mark used by a writer to show a pause in a sentence

_____ 5. a person who has seen or heard something

_____ 6. a plant with a large yellow or white root that is eaten as a vegetable

_____ 7. a player who hits hard in baseball; also a fighter who swings out with his fists

_____ 8. a short story with a moral

_____ 9. a slang word meaning a mighty blow with the fist

_____ 10. a store that sells food and household items

_____ 11. a surprise attack made from a concealed place

_____ 12. an order commanding people to retire from the streets at a certain time

_____ 13. another word for coward

_____ 14. talk about other people behind their backs

_____ 15. the body of a human or animal wrapped in a certain way after death

2 **Word Study.** Write the best answer on the line.

1. Edward's pants were so ＿＿＿＿＿＿ that he looked overweight.
   (a) baggy   (b) cheap   (c) dressy   (d) snazzy

2. If Lynne weren't so ＿＿＿＿＿＿, her monthly phone bills wouldn't be so high.
   (a) gabby   (b) grubby   (c) petty   (d) snippy

3. Stuart felt so ＿＿＿＿＿＿ that he thought he was going to faint.
   (a) cheerful   (b) cocky   (c) dizzy   (d) snippy

4. Lance was so ＿＿＿＿＿＿ about his clothes that if anyone so much as touched them, he flew into a rage.
   (a) careful   (b) concerned   (c) fussy   (d) fuzzy

5. Louise was so ＿＿＿＿＿＿ for Louis's help that she invited him over for dinner.
   (a) dejected   (b) grateful   (c) indecent   (d) needy

6. Mr. Duke received an ＿＿＿＿＿＿ message to call his wife at once.
   (a) distressful   (b) orderly   (c) typewritten   (d) urgent

7. Reed went to the movies so ＿＿＿＿＿＿ that he didn't know the names of any well-known movie stars.
   (a) early   (b) gladly   (c) often   (d) rarely

8. Lucy's mashed potatoes were so ＿＿＿＿＿＿ that everyone at the table found them difficult to chew.
   (a) delicious   (b) lumpy   (c) salty   (d) tasteless

9. The Cub Scouts were in terror as they listened to their leader tell a ＿＿＿＿＿＿ tale about a bear that had eaten five campers.
   (a) boring   (b) difficult   (c) grisly   (d) juicy

10. The Joneses decide to try to be less wasteful and take their newspapers, bottles, and tin cans to

    the ＿＿＿＿＿＿ center instead of putting them in the garbage.
    (a) recovery   (b) recycling   (c) refreshment   (d) restoring

11. The worm was so ＿＿＿＿＿＿ that Nick had a difficult time getting it onto the hook.
    (a) fatty   (b) oily   (c) spiny   (d) wiggly

12. In spite of many false starts, Louis Braille ＿＿＿＿＿＿ in his efforts to invent a successful system of reading and writing for the blind.
    (a) performed   (b) permitted   (c) persisted   (d) perspired

13. When June realized that all her new employer expected from her was that she agree with him about

    everything, she promptly began to look for a new job in which she wouldn't feel like a ＿＿＿＿＿＿.
    (a) mummy   (b) puppet   (c) rabbit   (d) typist

14. Although some people thought the king was an utter fool, others admired him greatly for his

vast _____.
   (a) fitness   (b) pettiness   (c) welfare   (d) wisdom

15. Linda's grandchildren had all been born in _____, Texas, in the 1960's.
   (a) Atlanta   (b) Cleveland   (c) Dallas   (d) Honolulu

3 **Which Word Does Not Fit?** Choose the word that does not fit with the rest and write it
on the line.

1. band	banjo	drums	flute	trumpet	_____
2. onions	cabbage	potatoes	turnips	french fries	_____
3. wren	blue jay	sparrow	vulture	woodpecker	_____
4. soap	soapy	perfume	shampoo	toothpaste	_____
5. dishpan	dishrag	dishtowel	bathrobe	potholder	_____
6. altar	Bible	hymnbook	preacher	Sunday	_____
7. naw	gosh	gee whiz	gnaw	golly	_____
8. buyer	goods	consumer	seller	customer	_____
9. god	goddess	princess	waitress	saleswoman	_____
10. blue	gloomy	dejected	depressed	involved	_____
11. silk	cotton	nylon	tweed	buttonhole	_____
12. cigar	opium	cocktail	tobacco	drugstore	_____
13. gossip	talker	busybody	darling	chatterbox	_____
14. ambush	choke	smother	strangle	throttle	_____
15. golf	hockey	tricycle	volleyball	basketball	_____

4 **Syllables.** Write each word in syllables on the line to the right. The number tells you how many syllables are in each word. Study the example before you begin.

1. monthly (2)   _month·ly_____

2. lonesome (2) _____

3. wiggle (2) _____

4. edgewise (2) _____

5. umpire (2) _____

6. sorrowful (3) _____

7. highchair (2) _____

8. senseless (2) _____

9. applesauce (3) _____

10. rightful (2) _____

11. singsong (2) _____

12. regardless (3) _____

13. improvement (3) _____

14. tender (2) _____

15. carelessness (3) _____

16. disappointment (4) _____

5 **Find the Quote.** Can you find this quote about how to treat people?

A. Each of the eleven sentences defines or gives a clue for a certain word. Write that word on the lines to the left of each sentence.

B. Put the letters of these words in the blanks at the bottom of the page. The quote, when all the blanks are filled in, will be a thought about how people should be treated.

— — — — —
20 24 33 35 56

1. Most department stores have a lost and _____ office.

— — — — — — —
15 46 53 34 17 62 58

2. Some people believe that you can find a pot of gold at the end of this.

— — — — M — — —
47 6 38 5 31   14 30 43

3. This word describes a really bad dream that frightens you.

— — — — — — —
45 50 37 17 25 22 51

4. This is what people often get if they stay out in the sun too long.

— — — — — — —
48 6 60 40 61 15 9

5. In the sky on a clear night, you can see the Big and Little _____.

— — — — — — — —
39 54 19 28 22 48 21 8

6. The person or team whom everyone thinks will lose the game is called the _____.

— — — — — — —
 1 53 63 44 36 7 55

7. Waiters and waitresses depend on this in order to make a decent living.

— — — — — — —
10 32 65 18 41 3 59

8. The crime that a traitor commits is called _____.

— — — — — — — —
 4 11 49 57 13 42 64 65

9. This word is a synonym for choke or strangle.

— — — — — — — — — —
17 49 16 29 56 2 36 7 52 28 26

10. The person who earns the money that pays for the food and bills in the household is called the _____.

— — —
27 12 23

11. A slang expression for going to sleep is "hit the _____."

Quote: — — —   — — — — — —   — — — —   — — —   — — —
          1 2 3   4 5 6 7 8 9   10 11 12 13   14 15 16   17 18 19

— — —   — — — —   — — — — — :   — — — — — — —
20 21 22   23 24 25 26   27 28 29 30 31   32 33 34 35 36 37 38

— —   — — — — —   — — —   — — — — — — —
39 40   41 42 43 44 45   46 47 48   49 50 51 52 53 54 55

— — — —   — — — — — —
56 57 58 59   60 61 62 63 64 65

Word Index: Lessons 1-16

A
absent
A.D.
address
admire
advance
Aesop
ain't
airtight
alongside
aloud
altar
alter
ambush
ankle
annoy
antonym
apiece
applaud
applause
applesauce
appoint
appointment
argue
argument
arise
Arizona
arose
arrest
arrow
Atlanta
author
avenue

B
Bacchus
backward
ban
banjo
barbecue
bathmat
bathrobe
battered
beating
beech
beyond
bile
birthplace
birthstone
blab
blare
blankly
blaze
bleacher
blessed
blimp
bloodhound

blond(e)
bloodshed
blowtorch
blubber
blueberry
blue jay
blur
boastful
boldness
bonnet
boost
bother
bout
boycott
boyfriend
Braille, L.
brat
breach
breadbox
breadwinner
brighten
brightness
brim
brisk
briskly
brittle
brood
broomstick
broth
brother-in-law
brushoff
budge
budget
burden
burnt
buttermilk
butterscotch
button
buttonhole
buyer
bye
bye-bye
bypass
bystander

C
cabin
cabinet
cactus
calf
canteen
capital
capitalize
carefully
carelessly
carelessness
carfare

Carl
carload
carrot
carton
cartoon
cask
casket
castor oil
catchy
category
cautiously
cease
ceasefire
ceaseless
census
chairman
champ
chant
chap
chapel
character
charcoal
chatter
chatterbox
check-out
cheekbone
cherry
Chicago
childish
chock
chooser
Chris
christen
Christlike
Christopher
chuck
chuckle
Cincinnati
cinnamon
cite
citizen
citizenship
clack
clamp
clatter
clause
cleanse
cleanser
cleat
Cleveland
clinch
cling
clink
clog
closely
closeness
clot

clove
clover
clump
cocktail
coffeepot
coffin
coldly
Colorado
colorblind
Columbus
comma
company
compact
contest
coon
coop
core
correct
correctly
costliness
cotton
cottonmouth
coward
craft
cram
crank
creak
creaky
creed
creek
crept
crest
cripple
croak
crossbar
crossroad
cruel
Cuba
cucumber
cuddle
cue
curfew
cuss
custard
cycle
cyclone

D
Dallas
damage
darkness
darling
daze
day-care
daylight
deathly
deceased

decent
decently
decision
decoy
deeply
dejected
Denver
department
depression
dictionary
differ
difficult
dirt-cheap
disable
disappoint
disappointment
disaster
disclose
discomfort
discount
discussion
diseased
disgrace
disgraceful
disgracefully
disobey
disorderly
disperse
distressful
dizzy
doom
dorm
doubt
doubtful
dove
draft
drawbridge
drawstring
dredge
dressy
drifter
drive-in
droop
dropout
druggist
drunken
duty
dye

E
eager
earnings
earthquake
ease
eastern
easygoing
edgewise

Edward
effort
eggplant
Elizabeth
elsewhere
employ
employee
emptiness
engine
engineer
enlarge
envelope
equal
equally
error
errorless
estate
evil
excitement
explosion
export
expression
eyebrow

F
fable
factory
feature
feedback
fellow
fender
fern
first aid
first-rate
fitness
flabby
flatly
flatten
flatter
flattery
flex
flick
Florida
floss
flown
flung
foam
foamy
follow
follower
footpath
footstep
fore
forecast
forever
forehead
former

fountain
fraction
frail
fraud
Fred
free-for-all
freehand
Frenchman
fret
friendless
friendliness
frightful
fringe
fro
frost
frostbite
frosting
fruitful
fruitless
fruity
fumble
furry
fussbudget
fussiness
fuzz
fuzziness
fuzzy

G
gab
gabby
gaily
gallbladder
galoshes
gamble
gambler
gap
gape
gargle
garlic
gash
gasp
gee-whiz
Genesis
Georgia
gerbil
ghost
gifted
gift-wrap
gig
giggle
gingerly
gingersnap
gladly
glassful
glaze
Glen

glider
glittery
glob
glory
glum
goad
goat
goddess
goggles
golf
good-bye
good night
gossip
granddaughter
grandpa
grandson
grandstand
grant
grasp
grate
grateful
greediness
Greenland
greyhound
grim
grizzly
grocery
groin
groove
groovy
grope
grouchiness
grubby
gunshot
gush
gym
gymnasium
gyp
gypsy

H
hag
hailstorm
half-wit
Halloween
handkerchief
hardworking
harness
haste
hatless
hawk
haymaker
haze
haziness
hazy
headlight
headline

head-on
headphone
headway
heal
heaviness
heavyset
hectic
he's
highchair
highly
hitch
hoax
hockey
hollow
homonym
Honolulu
hoot
horror
horseshoe
host
hotly
hound
housebroken
humid
humor
humorous
hutch
hymn
hymnbook

I
ignite
ignore
Illinois
illness
impact
impatience
impossible
improvement
incision
incite
incorrect
indecent
inner
insane
installment
insult
insurance
insure
intelligence
intelligent
intensely
interest
interesting
investment
invitation

ironmaster
issue

J
jag
jagged
jellybean
jersey
jewel
jeweler
jig
jiggle
Jimmy
joyfully

K
keen
keenly
Kenneth
kettle
kidney
kindly
kitten

L
ladder
lain
lantern
lawsuit
lease
length
lettuce
license
lightheaded
lion
litter
livestock
loafer
loan shark
loin
London
lonesome
loop
loophole
loot
looter
Los Angeles
loudmouth
Louis
lowland
Lucy
lumber
lumpiness
lumpy
lye
lynch
Lynn(e)

M
madam
madhouse
Maine
mama
manage
mane
mare
Margaret
margin
marker
market
marketplace
Mars
marsh
marshmallow
marshy
Maryland
Massachusetts
master
mattress
mayonnaise
meaningful
meantime
mellow
member
Memphis
mental
mercy
Miami
Midas
mill
mindful
miscall
mister
mixed
moneybags
monthly
moral
moreover
Moscow
moth
mothball
motherless
mount
mouthpiece
mummy
mustard
mutt
mystery

N
Nancy
napkin
naw
necessary
necklace

Neil
New Jersey
niece
nightmare
Nile
nit
nitwit
northeastern
northern
nosebleed
nutmeg
nylon

O
obey
oblong
obtain
odds
oily
ointment
Olson
opening
opportunity
orderly
organ
otherwise
outburst
outcry
outdoor
outfielder
outlaw
overjoyed
overpaid
overtook

P
package
palace
Pan
panhandle
panhandler
parcel
pardon
parent
Paris
parrot
parson
partner
pastime
patience
pavement
payroll
peak
peddler
pencil
per cent
perfect
perfume

permit
persist
perspire
pester
petal
pettiness
petty
pickup
pigsty
pillowcase
placement
plainclothes
planter
platform
playmate
playpen
playroom
pleasure
pliers
plop
pluck
plumber
ply
plywood
poise
poisoner
poisonous
pore
porter
pose
possible
post
postcard
postman
potholder
potpie
powder
power
powerhouse
prank
precise
predict
prepare
prescribe
pressure
prevent
preview
prick
prime
princess
prison
prod
producer
project
prowl
prowler
puddle

pulley
pullover
puppet
puppy
purple
puzzle
Pyrex

Q

quiz

R

rabbit
ranch
rancher
ransom
rap
rattle
reaction
ready-made
ready-to-wear
realize
rebirth
reborn
receipt
recent
recite
recline
recorder
recycle
reed
refer
refreshment
regardless
regret
reload
reminder
reorder
replace
replacement
repress
rescue
restore
restrain
reverse
review
revolve
revolver
reward
ribbon
riddle
rightful
rind
roadside
roam
roomful
roominess

roomy
roost
rooster
root
ruby
rudely
Russia
rye

S

safety
saint
saintly
saleswoman
salute
scab
scalp
scarce
scarcely
scatter
schoolhouse
schoolroom
schoolteacher
schooner
scoot
Scotland
scramble
scrapbook
scrawl
screwball
scribble
Scripture
sculpture
scum
Seattle
seldom
self-pity
seller
senseless
sermon
sh!
shabby
shall
shallow
shampoo
shed
shipshape
shirk
shiver
shoe
shoelace
shoestring
shoplifting
shortchange
showroom
shriek

shrine
shrivel
shrubbery
shrunken
shudder
shyness
sickness
sidestep
signal
silver
silverware
silvery
singsong
sissy
sister-in-law
sketchbook
sketchy
skillet
skim
skimp
skit
slack
slash
slate
slime
sliminess
slimy
slingshot
slit
slope
sloppiness
slosh
slug
slugger
slumber
slur
smallpox
smelly
smirk
smock
smother
smuggle
smuggler
snack bar
snare
snazzy
snipe
sniper
snippy
snitch
snowflake
snowy
snuff
soccer
solo
solve
somewhere

sorehead
sorrow
sorrowful
soul
southern
southwestern
soy
spar
spareribs
sparkle
sparrow
spearmint
speedway
spellbound
spike
spiny
splashdown
splashy
splatter
splendid
splendidly
splotch
splutter
sponsor
spotted
spotty
sprang
sprig
springtime
sprinkle
spruce
sprung
spun
spur
spurt
squad
squash
squawk
squeamish
squid
stab
stack
stag
stagger
stark
steadiness
steady
steeple
stench
stern
stickiness
stiff
stock
stole
stolen
stoplight
stormy

storybook
straightforward
strangle
strangler
strengthen
strep
stretcher
stride
strikeout
stringy
strive
strut
Stuart
stub
sty
style
stylus
suggest
suggestion
sunbather
supper
surfer
surround
survive
Susan
swank
sway
sweat shirt
sweetheart
sweetly
swelling
swimsuit
switchblade
swollen
swore
symptom
synonym
system

T

tackle
talker
tangle
tango
target
taut
taxi
teen
teenage
teenager
tempt
tender
tenderness
Tennessee
terror
thank you
thatched

thee
theirs
theme
thereabout
thereafter
they'd
they'll
thickness
thigh
thirteenth
thorough
thoroughly
thoughtfulness
thoughtlessness
thrash
thresh
thresher
thriller
throttle
throwaway
thrust
thruway
ticket
tinkle
toad
tobacco
toilet
toll
tollbooth
toothless
torch
totally
tract
trade-in
train wreck
traitor
treason
treasure
treasurer
treatment
treaty
trench
trespass
trespasser
tricycle
trigger
troublesome
trumpet
tummy
turnip
turnpike
twang
tweed
tweezers
twentieth
twig
twirl

twitch
type
typewriter
typewritten
typist

U

umpire
unaffected
unemployed
unequal
uniform
unimportant
unlighted
unlock
unnecessary
unseen
unsteady
unsuccessful
unsuited
upland
urge
urgent
urgently
usher

V

vain
valley
value
vampire
vast
vat
velvet
vent
Vermont
vet
veteran
veterinarian
volley
volleyball
vulture

W

wail
walnut
walrus
ware
warehouse

Washington, D.C.
watchdog
weakness
wealth
wealthy
welcome
welfare

well-to-do
wept
western
we've
wheelchair
whereabouts
where's
whiner
whiplash
whirlpool
whisper
whistle
White House
whop
whopper
wick
wiggle
wiggly
wildfire
willful
willingness
wisdom
wishbone
wishy-washy
wit
withdraw
witness
witty
woodchuck
wooden
workman
wrestle
wrestler

X

Y

yank
yeast
yep
yoke
yours
youth

Z

zebra
zigzag

Lesson 17

Common Word Endings

le	el	al	et	ic
chuckle	channel	total	faucet	picnic
uncle	flannel	formal	bucket	traffic
jungle	funnel	sandal	bullet	clinic
knuckle	tunnel	scandal	hornet	public
tumble	parcel	final	rocket	music

tion	sion	ture	ate	ish
station	expression	culture	chocolate	selfish
nation	mission	capture	private	Irish
lotion	permission	fracture	pirate	punish
motion	admission	lecture	climate	vanish
emotion	tension	structure	delicate	finish
section	vision	creature		

1 **Word Meanings.** Use the words at the left to fill in the blanks.

climate
delicate
flannel
funnel
hornet
knuckle
lecture
nation
pirate
private
punish
sandal
scandal
tension
vanish

_____ 1. a feeling of stress and strain

_____ 2. a formal talk given to a person, group, or class

_____ 3. a hollow cone with a tube extending from the smaller end for directing the downward flow of water, sand, etc.

_____ 4. a large insect that stings

_____ 5. a light slipper or low-cut shoe with a strap or straps

_____ 6. a soft cloth made of wool or a blend of wool and cotton

_____ 7. an act that brings about disgrace or really upsets the public

_____ 8. any joint of a finger

_____ 9. another word for country

_____ 10. frail; soft or gentle in touch and skill

_____ 11. not public

_____ 12. one who robs at sea without the permission of his country

_____ 13. the weather conditions of an area over a long period of time

_____ 14. to hurt someone for doing something wrong

_____ 15. to pass out of existence; to fade or decay to nothing

Words for Study

Rocco	promoter	garden	skitter
recess	Solly	aisle	whooped
Lily	career	sharpened	relief

He Swung and He Missed

It was Miss Beach who urged Rocco, in his fifteenth year, out of eighth grade and into the world. She had watched him fighting at recess times from his sixth year on. In his yearbook on the afternoon of his last day in school she wrote, "Trusting that Rocco will make good."

Rocco did make good in his own way. He stepped from the schoolroom into the ring back of the Happy Hour Bar. He fought through the middleweights and into the light-heavies, while his purses increased to as much as sixty dollars. When he was nineteen, he stopped growing, his purses stopped growing, and he married a girl called Lily.

He didn't win every one after that, and by the time he was twenty-two he was losing as often as he won. He fought on. It was all he could do. He never took a dive; he never had a setup or a soft touch. He stayed away from whisky; he never gambled; he went to bed early before every bout and he loved his wife. He fought in a hundred corners of the city, under a half dozen managers, and he fought every man he was asked to, at any hour. He never ran out on a fight and he was never put down for a ten-count. He took beatings from the best in the business, but he never stayed down for ten.

At the end, which came when he was twenty-nine, all he had left was his girl and his record of never having stayed down for ten. He went six weeks without earning a dime before he understood that he would have to give up either boxing or Lily. When he found her wearing a pair of his old tennis shoes about the house in order to save the heels on her one good pair of shoes, he made up his mind.

Maybe Rocco wasn't all that smart, but he wasn't punchy either. Just because there was a dent in his face from former bouts and bigger dents in his wallet, it didn't follow that his brain was dented. It wasn't. He knew what the score was. And he loved his girl.

So when Uncle Mike, a promoter, told Rocco that he had a twenty-year-old named Solly that he was bringing along under the billing of Kid Class, Rocco agreed to take a dive. After making this agreement, he left the gym with the biggest purse of his career. And it was the first purse he'd gotten in advance: four twenties and two tens.

He gave Lily every dime of that money. When he handed it over, he knew he was only doing the right thing for her. He had earned the right to sell out, and he had sold. The ring owed him more than a C-note, he reflected, as he added loudly for Lily's sake, "I'll stop the bum dead in his tracks."

They were both happy that night. Rocco had never been happier since leaving school.

His head hurt all the way to the City Gardens the night of the fight, but it let up a bit in the dressing room under the stands. As he started down the littered aisle and saw the lights of the ring, the pain sharpened once more.

He felt the robe being taken from his shoulders, and suddenly, in that one short moment before the bell, he felt more tired than he ever had in a ring before. He went out in a half-crouch and someone called out, "Cut him down, Solly."

He backed to make the boy lead, and then came in long enough to flick his left twice into the teeth and skitter away. The bleachers whooped, sensing blood. He'd give them their money's worth for a few rounds, anyhow. No use making it look too bad.

The great strength of a fighting man is his pride. That was Rocco's strength in the rounds that followed. The boy called Kid Class couldn't keep him down. Between the seventh and eighth round, Uncle Mike climbed into the ring beside young Rocco. He said nothing. Just stood there looking down. He thought Rocco might have forgotten. He'd had four chances to stay down and he hadn't taken one. Rocco looked up. "I'm clear as a bell," he told Uncle Mike. He hadn't forgotten a thing.

It wasn't until the tenth round that Rocco realized he wanted to knock the boy out. He'd been shortchanged since he left school; let them be on the short end tonight. She had the hundred—he'd get a job and forget every one of them. He'd end like he'd started, as a fighting man.

Rocco bulled the boy into the ropes and felt the boy fade sideways. Then Rocco caught him in the short ribs with his left. Solly managed somehow to hook his right hard to the button. Then the left. Rocco's mouthpiece went spinning. Kid Class came up fast behind him and threw the left under the armpit. Rocco went forward on the ropes and just hung there . . .

He came to in the locker room. Uncle Mike was somewhere near, telling him he had done fine, and then he was alone. He rose and dressed slowly, feeling a long relief that he'd come to the end. He'd done it the hard way, but he'd done it.

He was fixing his tie when Lily knocked. He called to her to come in. She tested the tape over his right eye shyly, fearing to hurt him with her touch, but wanting to be sure it wasn't loose. She was crying.

"I'm okay," he said. "There's nothin' wrong, honey." Then Rocco saw it wasn't that after all.

"You told me you'd win," Lily told him. "I got eight to one and put the whole damn bank roll on you. I wanted to surprise you, and now we ain't got a cryin' dime."

Rocco didn't blow up. He just felt a little sick. Sicker than he had ever felt in his life. He studied her from foot to head. His eyes didn't rest on her face; they went back to her one good pair of shoes. "You got good odds, honey," he told her thoughtfully. "You done just right. We made them sweat all night for their money." Then he looked up and grinned. A wide, white grin.

That was Rocco. He always did it the hard way; but he did it. Miss Beach would have been proud.

Adapted from "He Swung and He Missed" by Nelson Algren. Reprinted by permission of Donadio & Ashworth, Inc.

2 **About the Story.** Answer these questions in good sentence form.

1. Why does Uncle Mike enter the ring during Rocco's bout with Kid Class?

_____

2. Lily's shoes are mentioned twice in this story. Explain how, in each case, the shoes help Rocco make up his mind about something.

   a. _____

   b. _____

3. What do you think of Lily? Be sure to include some details to back up what you think.

_____

_____

4. How does the way in which Rocco loses the bout with Kid Class give the story a "happy ending"?

_____

_____

5. Why do you suppose the author says at the end of the story that Miss Beach would have been proud of Rocco?

_____

_____

6. How do you think the author feels about Rocco? Cite at least one example to back up what you think.

_____

_____

3 **Compound Words.** Choose a word from **List A** and add a word from **List B** to it to complete the sentences.

List A	List B
country	back
hand	bugs
honey	how
hop	kettle
litter	ladder
quarter	moon
quick	sand
rattle	scotch
some	side
step	snake
tea	work
team	written

1. As he walked nervously up the aisle with his new bride, the groom hoped that, _____, she would understand that they just couldn't afford the _____ right now because he had just spent everything he had saved for it on a Rolls Royce.

2. Ms. Edwards sent a _____ note to Carl's first grade teacher explaining that he had fractured his arm while playing _____ and would not be in school the rest of the week.

3. The coach glared at the _____ and said, "You know, this isn't a one-man show; and, unless you understand that we can only win this game through _____, we might as well throw in the towel right now."

4. To escape the dirt and grime of the city streets, the Olsons decided to go for a drive, but the _____, covered with bottles and trash thrown here and there by _____, thoroughly disgusted them as well.

5. While waiting for the _____ to whistle, Grandpa climbed the _____ to get a jar of Grandma's strawberry jam from the top shelf of the pantry.

6. With all her might, Mary was trying to pull her cousin out of the _____ when the hiss of a _____ frightened her, and she let go of the rope.

4 **Review of Word Sounds.** Choose the word in the line that has a different sound than the underlined letters in the first word. Write it on the line.

1. **fountain:** certain   curtain   mountain   remains   _____

2. **relief:**   belief   believe   preview   relieve   _____

3. **flower:**   brow   brownie   flow   flowerpot   _____

4. **Dutch:**   Butch   clutch   crutch   hutch   _____

5. **cargo:**   galoshes   gill   grudge   jug   _____

6. **enough:**   cough   rough   roughly   tough   _____

7. **loot:**   nook   noose   scoop   tooth   _____

8. **Easter:**   dreadful   dreamy   ease   feast   _____

9. **eager:**   area   creaky   weakness   yeast   _____

10. **ready:**   pleasure   tread   unsteady   league   _____

5 **If Rocco Had . . .** Choose the best answer for each of the following statements and write it on the line.

1. If Rocco had won the fight with Kid Class, he might later have felt _____.
   (a) boastful   (b) guilty   (c) only human   (d) outstanding

2. If news of Rocco's deal with Uncle Mike had leaked to the press, there might have been

   a _____.
   (a) decision   (b) free-for-all   (c) reward   (d) scandal

3. If Rocco decided to continue his boxing career, he might do exercises to improve his

   _____.
   (a) footwork   (b) homework   (c) piecework   (d) teamwork

4. If Uncle Mike asked Rocco to fight again, Rocco might consider it _____.
   (a) an honor   (b) easy money   (c) important   (d) too risky

5. If Rocco saw a loophole in his contract, he might see a _____.
   (a) boxer   (b) lawyer   (c) producer   (d) promoter

6. If Rocco had been smart in school, he might have been called _____.
   (a) a copycat   (b) a dropout   (c) a dumbbell   (d) an egghead

7. If Rocco always dropped the ball during gym class, his classmates might have called

him _____.
   (a) buttercup   (b) butterfingers   (c) butterfly   (d) butterscotch

8. If Rocco had finished high school, his picture would be in the _____.
   (a) notebook   (b) passbook   (c) scrapbook   (d) yearbook

9. If Rocco were trying to lose weight, he might eat _____.
   (a) Cheerios   (b) chicken broth   (c) spaghetti   (d) yogurt

10. If Rocco wanted to feel more relaxed, he might study _____.
    (a) French   (b) history   (c) math   (d) yoga

11. If Rocco had made it big and later bought an estate, he might hire a _____.
    (a) bartender   (b) doorman   (c) gardener   (d) promoter

12. If Rocco wanted to see the Boardwalk, he would go to _____.
    (a) Atlantic City   (b) Pearl Harbor   (c) Port Huron   (d) Dead Sea

13. If Rocco had a bout in Cincinnati, he would fly to _____.
    (a) Illinois   (b) Ohio   (c) Tennessee   (d) Vermont

14. If Rocco wanted to visit Egypt, he would go to _____.
    (a) Africa   (b) Asia   (c) North America   (d) South America

15. If Rocco wanted to visit the place where Jesus was born, he would go to _____.
    (a) Bethlehem   (b) Egypt   (c) Italy   (d) Jamestown

Lesson 18

Common Word Endings

le	al	tion	sion	et
candle	emotional	education	mansion	bracket
startle	personal	vacation	version	cricket
needle	informal	promotion	passion	socket
wrinkle	magical	commotion	compassion	closet
tickle	musical	situation	occasion	scarlet

age	ish	ic	ice	ive
courage	furnish	plastic	notice	active
encourage	British	elastic	justice	talkative
storage	publish	fantastic	service	relative
language	ticklish	electric	crevice	sensitive
advantage	stylish	Catholic	lattice	detective
marriage	sheepish			

1 Word Meanings.

A. Match the synonyms.

British

closet

crevice

fantastic

mansion

passion

relatives

scarlet

sheepish

startle

talkative

vacation

_____ 1. crack

_____ 2. English

_____ 3. large, beautiful house

_____ 4. gabby

_____ 5. holiday

_____ 6. kinfolk

_____ 7. red

_____ 8. scare

_____ 9. shy

_____ 10. small room for storage

_____ 11. strong feeling

_____ 12. unbelievable

B. Match the antonyms.

active

encourage

fantastic

furnished

justice

informal

mansion

sensitive

sheepish

stylish

talkative

wrinkled

_____ 1. bare

_____ 2. bold

_____ 3. commonplace

_____ 4. discourage

_____ 5. formal

_____ 6. injustice

_____ 7. mute

_____ 8. numb

_____ 9. shabby

_____ 10. shack

_____ 11. resting

_____ 12. smooth

Words for Study

Thor	confirm	finally	quietly
priest	attended	recognized	downcast
baptize	banns	ah	custom
Finn	Karen Bergman	invested	holy

The Father

The man whose story is told here was the wealthiest and most important person in his town. His name was Thor Olson. He entered the priest's study one day, tall and grave.

"I have gotten a son," said he, "and I wish to present him to be baptized."

"What shall his name be?" inquired the priest.

"Finn—after my father."

"And the sponsors?" the priest asked.

They were mentioned and proved to be the best men and women of Thor's relatives in the town.

"Is there anything else?" inquired the priest as he looked up.

Thor paused for a moment.

"I should like very much to have him baptized by himself," said he at last.

"On a weekday?"

"No," responded Thor. "Next Saturday at twelve o'clock noon."

"Is there anything else?" inquired the priest a second time.

"There is nothing else," and Thor twirled his cap as though he were about to go.

Then the priest rose. "There is yet this, however," said he and walking toward Thor, he took him by the hand and looked gravely into his eyes: "God grant that the child may become a blessing to you!"

One day sixteen years later, Thor stood once more in the priest's study.

"Really, you carry your age extremely well, Thor," said the priest for he saw no change whatever in the man.

"That is because I have no troubles," replied Thor.

To this the priest said nothing, but after a while he asked, "What is your pleasure this evening?"

"I have come this evening about that son of mine who is going to be confirmed tomorrow."

"He is a bright boy," remarked the priest.

"I did not wish to pay the priest until I heard what number the boy would have when he takes his place in church tomorrow," stated Thor.

"He will stand number one."

"So I have heard, and here is ten dollars for the priest."

"Is there anything else I can do for you?" inquired the priest, fixing his eyes on Thor.

"There is nothing else."

Thor went out.

Eight years more rolled by. Then one day a noise was heard outside the priest's study; many men were entering and at their head was Thor.

"You come well attended this evening, Thor," said the priest.

"I am here to request that the banns may be published for my son. He is about to marry Karen Bergman, daughter of the man who stands here beside me."

"Why, that is the richest girl in town."

"So they say," replied Thor, stroking back his hair with one hand.

The priest sat a while as if in deep thought. He then entered the names in his book without making any comments, and the men signed their names underneath. Thor laid three dollars on the table.

"One is all I am to have," said the priest.

"I know that very well, but he is my only child. I want to do it handsomely."

The priest took the money. "This is now the third time, Thor, that you have come here because of your son."

"But now I am through with him," said Thor, and folding up his pocketbook he said farewell and walked away.

The men slowly followed him.

Two weeks later the father and son were rowing across the lake one calm, still day to the Bergmans to make plans for the wedding.

"This oarlock is not tight," said the son who stood up to tighten it. At the same moment the board he was standing on slipped from under him. He threw out his arms, uttered a cry, and fell overboard.

"Take hold of the oar!" shouted the father, springing to his feet and holding out the oar. But when the son had made a few efforts, he grew stiff.

"Wait a moment!" shouted the father and began to row toward his son. Then the son rolled over on his back, gave his father one long look, and sank.

Thor could scarcely believe it. He held the boat still and stared at the spot where his son had gone down, as though he must surely come to the top once again. There rose some bubbles, then some more, and finally one large one that burst. The lake again lay there as smooth and bright as a mirror.

For three days and three nights people saw the father rowing round and round the spot without taking either food or sleep. He was dragging the lake for the body of his son. Toward morning of the third day he found it and carried it in his arms up over the hills to his home.

It might have been about a year from that day when the priest, late one autumn evening, heard someone outside the door carefully trying to find the latch. The priest opened the door and in walked a tall thin man with bowed form and white hair. The priest looked long at him before he recognized him. It was Thor.

"Are you out walking so late?" said the priest and stood in front of him.

"Ah, yes! it is late," said Thor and took a seat.

The priest sat down also, as though waiting. A long, long quiet followed. At last Thor said: "I have something with me that I should like to give to the poor. I want it to be invested in my son's name."

He rose, laid some money on the table and sat down again. The priest counted it.

"It is a great deal of money," said he.

"It is half the price of my land. I sold it today."

The priest sat quietly for a long time. At last he gently asked, "What do you plan to do now, Thor?"

"Something better."

They sat there for a while, Thor with downcast eyes, the priest with his eyes fixed on Thor. Presently the priest said slowly and softly: "I think your son has at last brought you a true blessing."

"Yes, I think so myself," said Thor, looking up, while two big tears ran slowly down his cheeks.

Adapted from "The Father" by Bjornstjerne Bjornson.

2 **About the Story.** Answer these questions in good sentence form.

1. Thor visits the priest four times in this story. Give the reason for each visit in the order in which the visits took place.

   a. _____

   b. _____

   c. _____

   d. _____

2. State the changes that happen in Thor as a result of his son's death.

   a. How he looks: _____

   b. How he feels about money: _____

   _____

   c. How he probably plans to spend his time now: _____

   _____

3. Explain what you think the priest means when he says, "I think your son has at last brought you a true blessing."

   _____

   _____

3 **What Are Banns?** Use the words at the left to fill in the blanks.

banns
bad
begun
church
holy
intend
marriage
members
opportunity
practiced
prevent
public
published
reason
1200

Banns are a _____ statement of the fact that a man and woman _____ to be married. The banns are read or _____ in _____.

This custom was _____ long ago to help _____ speedy or _____ matches between _____ of the church.

Reading them in public also gave people an _____ to object to the _____, if any good _____ were known.

In _____, it was ordered that _____ be published three times on three Sundays or _____ days in a row. The custom of reading or publishing banns is still _____ in some churches today.

4 Word Study. Complete the following sentences with the best answer.

1. Karen hoped that her parents would grant her _____ to fly to Florida with her girlfriend during spring vacation.
   (a) admission (b) commission (c) permission (d) remission

2. For many American children, Christmas morning is a truly _____ occasion.
   (a) commonplace (b) magical (c) startling (d) vanishing

3. In "The Star-Spangled Banner" the red glare is from _____.
   (a) lockets (b) pockets (c) rockets (d) sockets

4. Uncle Ted whistled at his beautiful wife as she showed him what she had bought during her latest shopping binge and exclaimed, "Not every woman can look as _____ as you in a flannel nightgown."
   (a) downcast (b) stylish (c) ticklish (d) wrinkled

5. Whenever Ginger _____, which was quite often, her face turned scarlet.
   (a) blushed (b) bothered (c) brooded (d) budged

6. The three bystanders _____ the fact that the engineer could not have avoided the accident and should in no way be blamed for the trainwreck.
   (a) confined (b) confirmed (c) conformed (d) controlled

7. Quite by accident, the detective _____ upon the clue that helped him crack the complex murder case.
   (a) bumbled (b) fumbled (c) stumbled (d) tumbled

8. With compassion in his eyes, the judge looked first at the husband and then at the wife before he remarked, "What we have here is a very delicate _____, and I'm sure neither of you will be pleased with the court's ruling."
   (a) advantage (b) existence (c) service (d) situation

9. Lily was so _____ poison ivy that just the sight of it made her feel itchy.
   (a) active in (b) covered with (c) relieved from (d) sensitive to

10. When the _____ realized the ship was about to sink, he stuffed his pockets with gold and jewels, jumped overboard, and promptly sank to the bottom of the deep blue sea.
    (a) pirate (b) private (c) traitor (d) trespasser

5 **Where Would You Find It?** Choose the word in each line that describes where you would most likely find the item listed first and write it to the right.

1. **mane:**   bobcat   lion   monkey   squirrel   _____

2. **cot:**   birthplace   dorm   laundromat   mansion   _____

3. **clinic:**   courthouse   grocery   hospital   library   _____

4. **rabbit:**   coop   hutch   kennel   sty   _____

5. **cherry:**   bulb   planter   tree   vine   _____

6. **porter:**   chapel   showroom   station   thruway   _____

7. **Nile:**   Egypt   Japan   Russia   Spain   _____

8. **compact:**   billfold   carton   knapsack   pocketbook   _____

9. **lattice:**   cupcake   doughnut   pie   pretzel   _____

10. **camel:**   desert   forest   jungle   meadow   _____

11. **postmark:**   envelope   letter   receipt   sketch   _____

12. **eggplant:**   field   garden   marsh   ranch   _____

13. **footpath:**   aisle   country   crossroad   traffic   _____

14. **cleats:**   galoshes   sandals   shoes   slippers   _____

15. **Dead Sea:**   Africa   Asia   Greenland   Holland   _____

Lesson 19 ━━━━━━━━━━━━━━━━━

The Sound for *ph*

In most words, the sound for **ph** is the same as the sound for **f**, as in *phone*, *Memphis*, and *alphabet*.

Phil	photo	physic	elephant	telephone
Philip	photograph	physics	trophy	microphone
Philadelphia	photography	physical	gopher	
Phyllis	photo finish	physician	prophet	
	photocopy	physique		
phantom	phase	graph	Ralph	
pharmacy	phrase	geography		

1 **Word Meanings.** Use the words at the left to fill in the blanks.

geography
gopher
graph
phantom
pharmacy
phase
Philadelphia
photo finish
photography
physician
physics
physique
prophet
trophy

_____ 1. a drawing used to display number relationships among items

_____ 2. a person who predicts what will happen; a person who speaks for God or a god as though he is being guided

_____ 3. a prize received for winning a race, contest, etc.

_____ 4. a race so close that the winner can be decided only from a photograph

_____ 5. a North American mammal about the size of a large rat and noted for its wide cheek pouches

_____ 6. another word for doctor

_____ 7. another word for drugstore

_____ 8. any stage in a cycle of growth

_____ 9. something feared or dreaded; something that seems to exist, but really has no physical form

_____ 10. the art or practice of taking and printing photographs

_____ 11. the structure or form of a body

_____ 12. the study of matter and energy

_____ 13. the study of the Earth's physical features

_____ 14. the American city often referred to as "the city of brotherly love"

Words for Study

Valentine	fondly	Annabel Adams	pal
warden	burglar	Spencer	lounged
cafe	burglary	needn't	selections
panel	tasteful	honest	inn

A Change of Heart: Part I

A guard came to the prison shoe shop where Jimmy Valentine was stitching shoes and took him to the front office. There the warden handed Jimmy his pardon.

"Now, Valentine," said the warden, "you'll go out in the morning. Brace up and make a man of yourself. You're not a bad fellow at heart. Stop cracking safes and live straight."

"Me?" said Jimmy, in surprise. "Why, I never cracked a safe in my life."

"Oh, no," laughed the warden. "Of course not. Take him back," smiled the warden to the guard, "and fix him up with clothes. Better think over my advice, Valentine."

At a quarter past seven the next morning Jimmy stood in the warden's office. He had on a suit and a pair of the stiff squeaky shoes that the state gives to its discharged guests.

Jimmy headed straight for a restaurant. From there he went to the train station. He tossed a quarter into the hat of a blind man sitting by the door and boarded his train. Three hours set him down in a little town near the state line. He went to the cafe and shook hands with Mike, who was alone behind the bar.

"Feeling all right?"

"Fine," said Jimmy. "Got my key?"

He got his key and went upstairs, unlocking the door of a room at the rear. Everything was just as he had left it. Pulling out from the wall a folding bed, Jimmy slid back a panel in the wall and dragged out a dust-covered suitcase. He opened this and gazed fondly at the finest set of burglar's tools in the East.

In half an hour Jimmy went downstairs and through the cafe. He was now dressed in tasteful and well-fitting clothes and carried his dusted and cleaned suitcase in hand.

A week after the release of Valentine, 9762, there was a neat job of safe-burglary done in a nearby city with no clue as to the author. Eight hundred dollars was taken. Two weeks after that a burglar-proof safe in another city was opened like a cheese to the tune of fifteen hundred dollars. The losses soon became high enough to bring the matter up into Ben Price's class of work.

"That's Jim Valentine's work," Price was heard to remark. "He'll do his bit next time without any short-time."

One afternoon Jimmy Valentine and his suitcase climbed out of the train in a little town down South. He went down the board sidewalk toward the hotel. A young lady crossed the street, passed him at the corner, and entered the bank. Jimmy Valentine looked into her eyes, forgot what he was, and became another man. She lowered her eyes and colored slightly.

Jimmy saw a boy loafing on the steps of the bank and began to ask him questions. He learned that the young lady's name was Annabel Adams and that her father owned the bank.

Jimmy went to the Planter's Hotel, signed the book as Ralph Spencer, and took a room. He leaned on the desk as he told the clerk that he had come here to look for a business opportunity. He had thought of the shoe business. Was there an opening?

The clerk was impressed by the clothes and manner of Jimmy. Yes, there ought to be a good opening in the shoe line. He hoped Mr. Spencer would decide to settle in the town. He would find it a nice place to live and the people were friendly.

Mr. Spencer thought he would stop over in the town a few days and look over the situation.

No, the clerk needn't call the boy. He would carry up his suitcase himself; it was rather heavy.

Mr. Spencer, who rose from Jimmy Valentine's ashes—ashes left by the flame of a sudden attack of love that completely changed him—remained in town and did very well. He opened a shoe store and enjoyed a good run of trade. At the end of a year his situation was this: he had won the respect of the townspeople, his shoe store was doing well, and he and Annabel were going to be married in two weeks.

One day Jimmy sat down in his room and wrote this letter, which he mailed to the safe address of an old friend.

Dear Old Pal:

I want to make you a present of my kit of tools. I know you'll be glad to get them. I've quit the old business. I've got a nice store, I'm making an honest living, and I'm going to marry the finest girl on earth two weeks from now. Be sure to be at Solly's next Wednesday night at nine o'clock, for I must see you. I'll bring along the tools.

　　　　Your old friend,

　　　　　　Jimmy

On the Monday night after Jimmy wrote this letter, Ben Price jogged into town in a buggy. He lounged about town until he found out what he wanted to know. From the drugstore across the street from Spencer's shoe store he got a good look at Ralph Spencer.

"Going to marry the banker's daughter are you, Jimmy?" said Ben to himself softly. "Well, I don't know!"

Continued in the next lesson . . .

Adapted from "The Retrieved Reformation" by O. Henry with permission of Airmont Publishing Company, Inc. New York, New York.

2 **About the Story.** Choose the letter of the best answer and write it on the line.

_____ 1. Which word best describes the tone of voice Jimmy Valentine might be using with the warden?

    (a) cocky

    (b) honest

    (c) informal

    (d) sheepish

_____ 2. After Jimmy's release from prison, he promptly _____ .

    (a) follows the warden's advice

    (b) ignores the warden's advice

    (c) is confused by the warden's advice

    (d) thinks over the warden's advice

_____ 3. The fact that Annabel "colors slightly" when Jimmy sees her means that she is _____ .

    (a) afraid of strangers

    (b) blushing

    (c) flirting

    (d) not used to being admired

_____ 4. Which word best describes the hotel clerk's reaction to Jimmy?

    (a) bored

    (b) cautious

    (c) distrustful

    (d) impressed

_____ 5. When Jimmy learns that Annabel is the banker's daughter, _____ .

    (a) he falls in love with her

    (b) he sees this as an opportunity to crack a safe

    (c) he sees this as an opportunity to earn the respect of the townspeople

    (d) it doesn't seem to impress him one way or the other

_____ 6. Why do you suppose Jimmy decides to open a shoe store instead of some other kind of store?

    (a) He knows something about shoes.

    (b) He thinks this type of business will help him to gain the respect of the townspeople.

    (c) The hotel clerk gives him this idea.

    (d) There's an opening in the town for a shoe store.

_____ 7. How much time passes in this section of the story?

    (a) short time

    (b) three weeks

    (c) about six months

    (d) a little more than a year

_____ 8. Which statement offers no proof that this story takes place in former times?

    (a) Ben Price rides into town in a buggy.

    (b) Jimmy opens a shoe store in a little town.

    (c) One of the safes Jimmy cracks has eight hundred dollars in it.

    (d) The sidewalk in the town is made of boards.

_____ 9. A main theme in this story is _____.

    (a) love is a powerful force that can change a person's life

    (b) once a crook, always a crook

    (c) prison can teach people useful trades

    (d) starting a new life is difficult

3 **What Happens Next?** In good sentence form, describe in detail what you think will happen next in "A Change of Heart."

_____

_____

_____

_____

_____

4 **Subjects for Study.** Match the words at the left with the subject in which they are studied.

authors
battles
commas
deserts
energy
explorers
force
fractions
Adolf Hitler
Jamestown
matter
mountains
numbers
per cents
power
rivers
sums
syllables
valleys
writing

English

1. _____
2. _____
3. _____
4. _____

Math

1. _____
2. _____
3. _____
4. _____

Geography

1. _____
2. _____
3. _____
4. _____

History

1. _____
2. _____
3. _____
4. _____

Physics

1. _____
2. _____
3. _____
4. _____

5 **Which Answer Fits Best?** Fill in the blanks with the best answer.

1. Pharmacy is to drugs as bakery is to _____.
   (a) dough   (b) baked goods   (c) rolling pin   (d) yeast

2. Capture is to release as repair is to _____.
   (a) broken   (b) damage   (c) mend   (d) useless

3. Brains are to student as _____ is to wrestler.
   (a) contests   (b) mat   (c) physique   (d) trophies

4. Needle is to dressmaker as _____ is to plumber.
   (a) wrench   (b) kitchen   (c) sink   (d) water

5. Dove is to peace as scales are to _____.
   (a) bathroom   (b) checkup   (c) justice   (d) overweight

6. Cactus is to desert as lion is to _____.
   (a) cage   (b) jungle   (c) grassy plain   (d) zoo

7. Waitress is to tip as saleswoman is to _____.
   (a) budget   (b) commission   (c) public   (d) wages

8. Gypsy is to roam as _____.
   (a) guide is to lead   (c) relative is to visit
   (b) physician is to clinic   (d) umpire is to home plate

9. Restaurant is to dining as _____.
   (a) altar is to marriage   (c) garden is to digging
   (b) closet is to storing   (d) traffic is to tension

10. Courage is to hero as _____.
    (a) coward is to fear   (c) pictures are to photographer
    (b) fear is to coward   (d) prophet is to Bible

6 **A Circle Graph.** One of the new words in this lesson is *graph*. A graph is a quick way to get an idea of what's happening in a certain area or situation. The type of graph you see on this page is called a circle graph. Study the graph and answer the questions. (Note: In a circle graph, the total of items is always 100%.)

Diners' Selections at the Harbor Inn, 1985

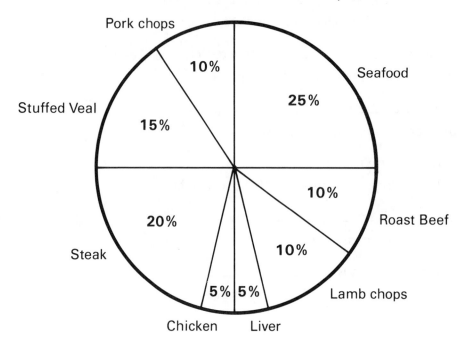

1. What per cent of the diners who ate dinner at the Harbor Inn in 1985 ordered liver? _____

2. Which two items on the menu were chosen least often in 1985 at the Harbor Inn? _____

   and _____

3. How many items on the menu were chosen as often as pork chops? _____ Name them: _____

   _____

4. _____ times as many people chose seafood as liver.
   (a) Three   (b) Four   (c) Five   (d) Six

5. _____ as many people chose steak as chose lamb chops.
   (a) One half   (b) One quarter   (c) Three times   (d) Twice

6. _____ as many people chose liver as chose roast beef.
   (a) One half   (b) One quarter   (c) Three times   (d) Twice

7. Which two items on the menu were chosen most often? _____ and _____

8. Does this graph tell you how many people ate dinner at the Harbor Inn in 1985? _____

9. Does this graph tell you which items on the menu cost the most money? _____

10. In what way would this graph be helpful to the manager of the Harbor Inn? _____

    _____

Lesson 20

Four-Letter Words

bawl	tidy	zero	veto	hula	ache
veil	bury	trio	diet	data	x-ray
oath	navy	hobo	duet	Iowa	poem
debt	fuel	halo	omit	Erie	poet
chef	duel	echo	omen	Utah	amen

1 **Word Meanings.** Use the words at the left to fill in the blanks.

ache
amen
bawl
chef
debt
duet
Erie
hula
oath
omit
poet
tidy
veto
zero

_____ 1. a dance often performed in Hawaii

_____ 2. a dull, steady pain

_____ 3. a fancy word for a cook

_____ 4. a musical piece for two performers

_____ 5. a pledge, often calling upon God as a witness

_____ 6. money that is owed

_____ 7. nothing

_____ 8. one of the five Great Lakes

_____ 9. one who writes poems or verses

_____ 10. said at the end of a prayer

_____ 11. shipshape; extremely neat

_____ 12. to cry loudly

_____ 13. to forbid or prevent

_____ 14. to leave out; to fail to include

Words for Study

future	coolly	polite	combination
nickel-plated	vault	metal	panic
shoehorn	fastened	engaged	frantic

A Change of Heart: Part II

The next morning, Jimmy had breakfast with the Adamses. He was going to Little Rock that day to order his wedding suit and buy something nice for Annabel. That would be the first time he left town since he had come there more than a year ago. Because so much time had passed since those last "jobs," he thought it would be safe.

After breakfast a large family party went downtown together—Mr. Adams, Annabel, Jimmy, and Annabel's married sister with her two little girls, aged five and nine. They came by the hotel where Jimmy still boarded, and he ran up to his room and brought along his suitcase. Then they went on to the bank. There stood Jimmy's horse and buggy and Adolf, who was going to drive him over to the railroad station.

All went inside the high, carved oak railings into the banking room—Jimmy included, for Mr. Adams' future son-in-law was welcome anywhere. The clerks were pleased to be greeted by the good-looking, friendly young man who was going to marry Miss Annabel. Jimmy set his suitcase down. Annabel, whose heart was bubbling with happiness and lively youth, put on Jimmy's hat and picked up the suitcase. "Wouldn't I make a nice salesman?" asked Annabel. "My, Ralph, how heavy it is! Feels like it was full of gold bricks."

"Lots of nickel-plated shoehorns in there," said Jimmy coolly, "that I'm going to return. Thought I'd save express charges by taking them up. I'm getting awfully thrifty."

The bank had just put in a new safe and vault. Mr. Adams was very proud of it and insisted that everyone inspect it. The vault was a small one, but it had a new door. It fastened with three solid steel bolts and had a time lock. Beaming, Mr. Adams explained its workings to Mr. Spencer, who showed a polite but not too intelligent interest. The two children, May and April, were delighted by the shining metal and funny clocks and knobs.

While they were thus engaged, Ben Price strolled in and leaned on his elbow, looking coolly inside between the railings. He told the teller that he didn't want anything; he was just waiting for a man he knew.

Suddenly, there was a scream or two from the women, and a commotion. Unseen by the adults, May, the nine-year-old girl, in play, had shut April in the vault. She had then shot the bolts and turned the knob of the combination as she had seen her grandfather do.

The old banker sprang to the handle and tugged at it for a moment. "The door can't be opened," he groaned. "The clock hasn't been wound nor the combination set."

April's mother screamed again.

"Hush!" said Mr. Adams, raising a shaking hand. "All be quiet for a moment. April," he called as loudly as he could. "Listen to me." During the following quiet, they could just barely hear the faint sound of the child wildly screaming in the dark vault in a panic of terror.

"My dearest darling!" wailed the mother. "She will die of fright! Open the door! Oh, break it open! Can't you men do something?"

"There isn't a man nearer than Little Rock who can open that door," said Mr. Adams in a shaky voice. "My God! Spencer, what shall we do? That child—she can't stand it long in there. There isn't any air."

April's mother, frantic now, beat the door of the vault with her hands. Annabel turned to Jimmy, her large eyes full of pain, but not yet giving up hope.

He looked at her with a queer, soft smile on his lips and in his keen eyes. "Annabel," he said, "give me that rose you are wearing, will you?"

Hardly believing that she heard him correctly, she unpinned the bud from her dress and placed it in his hand. Jimmy stuffed it into the pocket of his vest, threw off his coat, and rolled up his sleeves. With that act Ralph Spencer passed away and Jimmy Valentine took his place.

"Get away from the door, all of you," he commanded shortly.

He set his suitcase on the table and opened it flat. From that time on, he seemed to be unaware of anyone else. He laid out the shining, queer tools swiftly and orderly, whistling softly to himself as he always did when at work. The others watched him as if under a spell.

Jimmy's pet drill was biting smoothly into the steel door. In ten minutes—breaking his own record—he threw back the bolts and opened the door.

April, on the verge of fainting, but safe, fell into her mother's arms.

Jimmy Valentine put on his coat and walked outside the railings toward the front door. As he went, he thought he heard a faraway voice that he once knew call "Ralph!" But he never stopped.

At the door a big man stood somewhat in his way.

"Hello, Ben!" said Jimmy, still with his strange smile. "Got around at last, have you? Well, let's go. I don't know that it makes much difference now."

And then Ben Price acted strangely.

"Guess you're mistaken, Mr. Spencer," he said. "Don't believe I know you. Your buggy's waiting for you, ain't it?"

And Ben Price turned and strolled down the street.

Adapted from "The Retrieved Reformation" by O. Henry with permission of Airmont Publishing Company, Inc. New York, New York.

2 **About the Story.** Answer the following questions in good sentence form.

1. Why does Jimmy have his burglar tools with him when he goes to the bank with the Adams family?

2. Why does Jimmy show "polite but not too intelligent interest" as Mr. Adams explains the workings of the safe?

3. Why do you think Ben Price changes his mind about arresting Jimmy Valentine?

4. What do you think would have happened in the story if Jimmy had not opened the safe?

5. If the story had continued, how do you think Annabel and her family would have reacted to learning about Jimmy's past?

3 **"Heartfelt" Expressions.** English contains many expressions which include the word *heart*. Complete the following sentences with the ten expressions listed below.

- after my own heart
- break my heart
- does my heart good
- have a heart
- heart's not in it

- from the bottom of my heart
- lost his heart to
- set his heart at rest
- take heart
- wear your heart on your sleeve

1. Accepting the trophy on behalf of the entire soccer team, the coach stepped up to the microphone and said tearfully, "I thank you all _____ ."

2. "Come on, Ms. Price, _____ !" groaned the class upon hearing that she expected them to know all fifty state capitals by Wednesday.

3. "_____ ," encouraged Ralph's music teacher to her very discouraged student. "If you persist for just a few more weeks, I know you'll perform just beautifully at the Christmas concert."

4. "No, Tom hasn't lost his mind," explained Ms. Sutter to her puzzled husband. "He's just _____ a lovely young woman he met last weekend at the ski lodge."

5. "It _____ to see that you finally took the doctor's advice and quit smoking," said Ralph to his mother.

6. As the grandfather proudly watched his young grandson struggle to pull the weeds from his garden, he said, "Now, there's a gardener _____ ."

7. Walter looked gravely at his wife and said sadly, "If our son doesn't start trying to make something of his life, he's going to _____ ."

8. Trying to explain to her boss why she was turning down the promotion, Susan said, "It would be unfair to the company because, even though I know I could do the work, my _____ ."

9. When the pirate had confessed his many sins to the priest, he felt that he had _____ and was now fully prepared to be punished by the court for his crimes.

10. "You know," Margaret said softly to Phyllis who lay sobbing on her bed, "if you just wouldn't _____ , you wouldn't get hurt like this so often."

4 **Valentine's Day Customs of Long Ago.** Use the words at the left to fill in the blanks.

bits
choice
contain
customs
early
husbands
keyholes
married
mates
objects
peep
regarding
scrap
unmarried
warned

Years ago, people held many beliefs _____ Valentine's Day.

One of the oldest beliefs said that birds choose their _____ on February 14.

An old English idea _____ that it was bad luck to bring snow into the

house before Valentine's Day if _____ girls in the home hoped to be

married before the end of the year.

Most Valentine's Day _____ were concerned with falling in love or

the _____ of a mate.

Single girls had many ways of learning who their _____ were going to be.

Sometimes a girl wrote her boyfriends' names on _____ of paper and rolled each

name into a little piece of clay. She then dropped the clay into water. The first

_____ of paper to rise to the top was said to _____ the name of

her true valentine.

Another custom was that young ladies rose _____ on February 14, looked

through their _____, and hoped to see two _____. If a girl

saw only one object in her first _____ through the keyhole, she was said to have

little chance of being _____ that year.

5 **Syllables.** Write the following words, in syllables, on the lines to the right.

1. duty _____

2. halo _____

3. oath _____

4. diet _____

5. navy _____

6. omen _____

7. holy _____

8. veto _____

9. solo _____

10. chef _____

11. fuel _____

12. echo _____

6 **Compound Words.** Fill in the blanks with the correct answers.

1. A fault or a flaw in a person's character is referred to as a _____.
   (a) shortcake   (b) shortcoming   (c) shortcut   (d) shorthand

2. A newcomer to a ranch or any person who is a beginner at something is called

   a _____.
   (a) barefoot   (b) flatfoot   (c) tenderfoot   (d) underfoot

3. A person who leads others in actions that are often unlawful is called a _____.
   (a) ringleader   (b) ringmaster   (c) ringside   (d) ringworm

4. A person who makes sure everybody is working very, very hard is referred to as

   a _____.
   (a) postmaster   (b) ringmaster   (c) scoutmaster   (d) taskmaster

5. A person who tends to behave in a cruel manner can be described as _____.
   (a) bloodshed   (b) bloodshot   (c) bloodstain   (d) bloodthirsty

6. A synonym for marriage is _____.
   (a) deadlock   (b) oarlock   (c) padlock   (d) wedlock

7. A tree, such as a pine, fir, or spruce, that remains green throughout the year is

   an _____.
   (a) everglade   (b) evergreen   (c) everlasting   (d) evermore

8. Shallow pits dug by men in combat to protect themselves against enemy fire are called

   _____.
   (a) foxholes   (b) keyholes   (c) knotholes   (d) potholes

9. This thin-walled tube which carries air to the lungs is called the _____.
   (a) bagpipe   (b) blowpipe   (c) drainpipe   (d) windpipe

10. When a person who gives a lecture gets _____, it's often difficult to understand
    what the point is.
    (a) sidelined   (b) sidestepped   (c) sideswiped   (d) sidetracked

Review: Lessons 1-20

1 **Twenty Questions.** Choose a word at the left to fill in each blank.

A.D.
John Adams
Aesop
Atlantic City
B.C.
Bacchus
banns
Bethlehem
boycott
Louis Braille
cabinet
Thomas Edison
Genesis
Germany
Midas
New York City
Philadelphia
physique
veto
George Washington

1. The Greek writer of fables is _____.

2. The Greek god of wine was _____.

3. The king in a Greek story who, at first, thirsted for gold was

   _____.

4. The first book of the Bible is _____.

5. The town in which Jesus was born is _____.

6. _____ is used to express time before the birth of Jesus.

7. _____ is used to express time after the birth of Jesus.

8. The first president of the United States was _____.

9. The second president of the United States was _____.

10. If the president doesn't agree with a bill, he can _____ it.

11. The president's _____ is made up of men and women who
    head the different departments and give the president advice.

12. The largest city in the United States is _____.

13. The "city of brotherly love" is _____.

14. The American city that is well-known for its Boardwalk is

    _____.

15. The country that was split into two countries after World War II ended is

    _____.

16. The American who invented the light bulb is _____.

17. The Frenchman who invented a system of reading for the blind

    is _____.

18. A _____ is a situation in which people stop using something or
    dealing with somebody because they want to force a change.

19. _____ refers to the structure and form of the body.

20. _____ are published to state that a man and woman intend to
    be married.

2 **Word Review.** Fill in the blank with the word that best completes the sentence.

1. "Don't worry, it's _____," said Lily just after her weekend guest had knocked the vase off the bookshelf by accident.
   (a) brittle   (b) elastic   (c) plastic   (d) vanished

2. As Carl waited to be treated for the injury he had received during the soccer game, his entire body _____ so badly, he was sure he would never be able to play another game.
   (a) ached   (b) jiggled   (c) spurted   (d) whooped

3. When Karen could no longer tell which niece was which, she realized that her eyesight was not as _____ as it used to be.
   (a) blurred   (b) eager   (c) keen   (d) mindful

4. The coach requested that the net be fixed so _____ practice could start on time.
   (a) golf   (b) hockey   (c) soccer   (d) volleyball

5. Before the guard had a chance to say even one word, the prowler started pleading, "Have _____ on me. Don't turn me in."
   (a) justice   (b) mercy   (c) passion   (d) self-pity

6. The student could not understand how he was ever going to learn the names of all the rivers in Asia for the _____ quiz.
   (a) English   (b) geography   (c) gym   (d) physics

7. At the lecture Tuesday night, the speaker made such an _____ on Jimmy that he decided to stop smoking just as soon as he finished his last pack of cigarettes.
   (a) advance   (b) explosion   (c) impact   (d) outburst

8. The inspector declared that the crew had done such a _____ repair job on the tracks that every single person should be fired.
   (a) perfect   (b) spotty   (c) thorough   (d) unbelievable

9. At the _____ moment that the telephone rang, someone started pounding on the front door, and Elizabeth didn't know which to respond to first.
   (a) hectic   (b) impossible   (c) precise   (d) urgent

10. Upon noticing how often his children used the computer he had just bought them, Fred decided he had made a wise _____.
    (a) improvement   (b) installment   (c) investment   (d) replacement

11. After having heard his employees explain how much ill feeling his new plan would cause, the manager decided to _____ his decision and continue using the former plan.
    (a) restrain   (b) reverse   (c) review   (d) revolve

12. "Don't mind her," said Mother as her teenage daughter stormed off to her bedroom and

slammed the door. "She's just going through a _____."
   (a) occasion   (b) phase   (c) phrase   (d) symptom

13. Lee was convinced that, if she just _____, her employer would give her a raise
    sooner or later.
    (a) bothered   (b) gossiped   (c) persisted   (d) survived

14. "This argument is really _____," exclaimed Margaret. "Who cares whether we serve
    turnips or squash for Thanksgiving dinner!"
    (a) ceaseless   (b) delicate   (c) petty   (d) personal

15. As the woman tripped over the coffee table, the photographer said, "I'm sorry, but I just don't think

you have the _____ necessary to pose for these pictures."
    (a) emotion   (b) physique   (c) poise   (d) safety

3 **Synonyms.** Match these synonyms.

alter	_____	1. broth
annoy		
brim	_____	2. casket
coffin		
disperse	_____	3. change
error		
frail	_____	4. country
hoax		
jewel	_____	5. top edge
marriage		
nation	_____	6. fraud
parcel		
prod	_____	7. fret
soup		
worry	_____	8. gem
	_____	9. goad
	_____	10. mistake
	_____	11. package
	_____	12. pester
	_____	13. scatter
	_____	14. weak
	_____	15. wedlock

4 Antonyms. Match these antonyms.

absent
blurred
cease
distressful
doubtful
faultless
holy
host
mountain
petty
roomy
scatter
uncle
wealthy
zigzag

_____ 1. aunt

_____ 2. certain

_____ 3. clear

_____ 4. collect

_____ 5. continue

_____ 6. cramped

_____ 7. flawed

_____ 8. guest

_____ 9. important

_____ 10. needy

_____ 11. present

_____ 12. relaxing

_____ 13. sinful

_____ 14. straight

_____ 15. valley

5 Homonyms. Complete the following sentences with the correct homonyms.

by *and* bye
1. "_____ and have a great time in Colorado," said Phyllis as she stood

_____ the gate and waved to her cousin.

in *and* inn
2. When a diner shouted "Fire!" in sheer panic, the dining room of the

_____ was empty _____ just a matter of seconds.

Fill *and* Phil
3. "_____ 'er up," said _____ proudly as everyone at the gas station
turned to admire his Rolls Royce.

him *and* hymn
4. "Even if he thinks it's no good, can't you convince _____ to sing the

_____ I wrote for the Easter service?" begged the parson.

ball *and* bawl
5. Glaring at his classmate, Solly said, "If you're going to _____ every

time I throw the _____ to someone else, you can't be on my team."

allowed *and* aloud   6. Even though he felt disappointed when his uncle told him he would not

be _____ to carry the gun on the hunting trip, Chris said _____, "That's okay. I'll just carry some of the camping gear."

main *and* mane   7. The _____ reason the horse's _____ looked so awful was that the groom had been ill for two weeks.

read *and* reed   8. Because John didn't bother to _____ the fine print, he damaged the

_____ in his English horn the very first time he used it.

peaked *and* peeked   9. When Ralph _____ between his fingers to see how his horse was

doing in the race, he groaned, "Oh, no, I think my horse _____ too soon!"

pore *and* pour   10. It seemed to Nancy that every _____ reacted in terror as the nurse

began to _____ the burning liquid onto her wound.

incite *and* insight   11. It didn't require much _____ on the part of the police officers to

recognize who would _____ the townspeople to form a lynch mob.

sole *and* soul   12. "Not a _____ will ever realize that my _____ reason for the crime was to see whether or not I could get away with it," chuckled the pirate.

6   **Word Sound Review.** Choose the word in each line that does *not* have the same sound as the underlined letters in the first word and write this word on the line.

1. **fr<u>ai</u>l:**	ag<u>ai</u>nst	f<u>ai</u>thful	r<u>ai</u>d	w<u>ai</u>stline	_____
2. **p<u>ea</u>k:**	b<u>ea</u>d	cl<u>ea</u>nse	l<u>ea</u>sh	p<u>ea</u>nut	_____
3. **l<u>oo</u>ter:**	b<u>oo</u>th	sh<u>oo</u>t	w<u>oo</u>dy	z<u>oo</u>	_____
4. **pill<u>ow</u>:**	b<u>ow</u>ling	ch<u>ow</u>	r<u>ow</u>boat	sh<u>ow</u>n	_____
5. **bl<u>ou</u>se:**	d<u>ou</u>ble	d<u>ou</u>btful	l<u>ou</u>nge	s<u>ou</u>rpuss	_____
6. **st<u>y</u>:**	b<u>y</u>stander	P<u>y</u>rex	st<u>y</u>le	s<u>y</u>mptom	_____
7. **zi<u>g</u>za<u>g</u>:**	tan<u>g</u>o	tar<u>g</u>et	underdo<u>g</u>	ur<u>g</u>ently	_____
8. **a<u>ch</u>e:**	bar<u>g</u>e	enga<u>g</u>e	poli<u>t</u>e	re<u>c</u>ipe	_____
9. **<u>Ch</u>ris:**	<u>ch</u>ild	<u>Ch</u>ristmas	<u>ch</u>rome	e<u>ch</u>o	_____
10. **<u>c</u>ustom:**	<u>c</u>itizen	<u>c</u>omma	deli<u>c</u>ate	garli<u>c</u>	_____

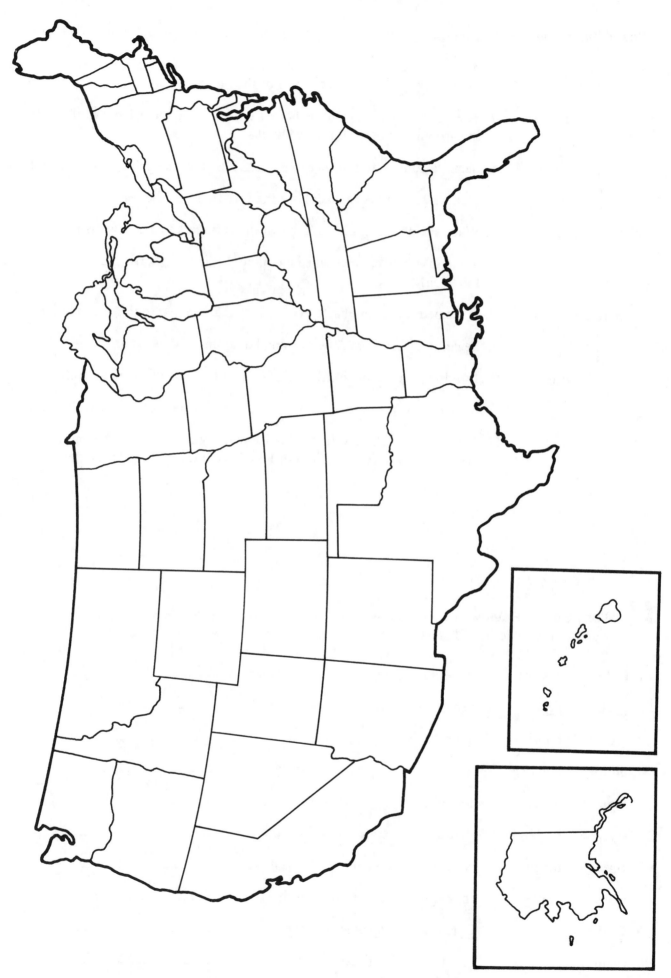

7 **United States Geography.** With the aid of a friend who knows his geography, or a United States map, put the following states in the correct places on the map. If you have time, put the remaining thirty states in the correct places.

Arizona	Georgia	Maine	New Hampshire	Texas
California	Hawaii	Maryland	New Jersey	Utah
Colorado	Illinois	Massachusetts	Ohio	Vermont
Florida	Iowa	Michigan	Tennessee	Washington

Word Index: Lessons 1-20

A
absent
ache
active
A.D.
Adams
address
admire
admission
advance
advantage
Aesop
ah
ain't
airtight
aisle
alongside
aloud
altar
alter
ambush
amen
ankle
Annabel
annoy
antonym
anyhow
apiece
applaud
applause
applesauce
appoint
appointment
area
argue
argument
arise
Arizona
armpit
arose
arrest
arrow
Atlanta
attend
author
avenue

B
Bacchus
backward
bagpipe
bakery
ban
banjo
banns
baptize
barbecue

barefoot
bathmat
bathrobe
battered
bawl
beating
beautifully
beech
behalf
Bergman
Bethlehem
beyond
bile
billing
birthplace
birthstone
blab
blare
blankly
blaze
bleacher
blessed
blimp
bloodhound
blond(e)
bloodshed
bloodshot
bloodstain
bloodthirsty
blowpipe
blowtorch
blubber
blueberry
blue jay
blur
boastful
bobcat
boldness
bonnet
boost
bother
bout
boycott
boyfriend
bracket
Braille, L.
brat
breach
breadbox
breadwinner
brighten
brightness
brim
brisk
briskly
British
brittle

brood
broomstick
broth
brother-in-law
brow
brushoff
budge
budget
bullet
bumble
burden
burglar
burglary
burnt
bury
businessman
buttercup
butterfingers
buttermilk
butterscotch
button
buttonhole
buyer
bye
bye-bye
bypass
bystander

C
cabin
cabinet
cactus
cafe
calf
candle
canteen
capital
capitalize
capture
career
carefully
carelessly
carelessness
carfare
Carl
carload
carrot
carton
cartoon
cask
casket
castor oil
catchy
category
Catholic
cautiously

cease
ceasefire
ceaseless
census
chairman
champ
chant
chap
chapel
character
charcoal
chatter
chatterbox
check-out
checkup
cheekbone
chef
cherry
Chicago
childish
chock
chooser
Chris
christen
Christ-like
Christopher
chuck
chuckle
Cincinnati
cinnamon
cite
citizen
citizenship
clack
clamp
classmate
clatter
clause
cleanse
cleanser
cleat
Cleveland
climate
clinch
cling
clinic
clink
clog
closely
closeness
closet
clot
clove
clover
clump
cocktail
coffeepot

coffin
coldly
Colorado
colorblind
Columbus
combat
combination
comma
commission
commonplace
commotion
compact
company
compassion
confirm
contest
coolly
coon
coop
core
correct
correctly
costliness
cotton
cottonmouth
countryside
courage
coward
craft
cram
crank
creak
creaky
creature
creed
creek
crept
crest
crevice
cricket
cripple
croak
crossbar
crossroad
cruel
Cub Scout
Cuba
cucumber
cuddle
cue
curfew
cuss
custard
custom
cycle
cyclone

D
Dallas
damage
damn
darkness
darling
data
daze
day-care
daylight
Dead Sea
deadlock
deathly
debt
deceased
decent
decently
decision
decoy
deeply
dejected
delicate
Denver
department
depression
detective
dictionary
diet
differ
difficult
direct
dirt-cheap
disable
disappoint
disappointment
disaster
disclose
discomfort
discount
discourage
discussion
diseased
disgrace
disgraceful
disgracefully
disobey
disorderly
disperse
distressful
distrustful
dizzy
doom
dorm
doubt
doubtful
dove

downcast
draft
drainpipe
drawbridge
drawstring
dreamy
dredge
dressmaker
dressy
drifter
drive-in
droop
dropout
druggist
drunken
duel
duet
dumbbell
duty
dye

E

eager
earnings
earthquake
ease
eastern
easygoing
echo
edgewise
education
Edward
effort
eggplant
elastic
electric
elephant
Elizabeth
elsewhere
emotion
emotional
employ
employee
emptiness
encourage
enemy
engage
engine
engineer
enlarge
envelope
equal
equally
Erie
error
errorless

estate
everglade
evergreen
everlasting
evermore
evil
excitement
existence
explosion
export
expression
eyebrow

F

fable
factory
fantastic
faraway
fasten
feature
feedback
fellow
fender
fern
fifteenth
final
finally
finish
Finn
first aid
first-rate
fitness
flabby
flannel
flatfoot
flatly
flatten
flatter
flattery
flaw
flex
flick
Florida
floss
flown
flung
foam
foamy
follow
follower
fondly
footpath
footstep
footwork
fore
forecast
forever

forehead
formal
former
fountain
fraction
fracture
frail
frantic
fraud
Fred
free-for-all
freehand
Frenchman
fret
friendless
friendliness
frightful
fringe
fro
frost
frostbite
frosting
fruitful
fruitless
fruity
fuel
fumble
funnel
furnish
furry
fussbudget
fussiness
future
fuzz
fuzziness
fuzzy

G

gab
gabby
gaily
gallbladder
galoshes
gamble
gambler
gap
gape
garden
gardener
gargle
garlic
gash
gasp
gee-whiz
Genesis
geography

Georgia
gerbil
ghost
gifted
gift-wrap
gig
giggle
gingerly
gingersnap
gladly
glassful
glaze
Glen
glider
glittery
glob
glory
glum
goad
goat
goddess
goggles
golf
good-bye
good night
gopher
gossip
granddaughter
grandma
grandpa
grandson
grandstand
grant
graph
grasp
grate
grateful
gravely
greediness
Greenland
greyhound
grim
grime
grizzly
grocery
groin
groove
groovy
grope
grouchiness
grubby
gunshot
gush
gym
gymnasium
gyp
gypsy

H

hag
hailstorm
half-wit
Halloween
halo
handkerchief
handsomely
handwritten
hardworking
harness
haste
hatless
hawk
haymaker
haze
haziness
hazy
headlight
headline
head-on
headphone
headway
heal
heartfelt
heaviness
heavyset
hectic
he's
highchair
highly
hitch
hoax
hobo
hockey
hollow
holy
homonym
honest
honeymoon
Honolulu
hoot
hopscotch
hornet
horror
horseshoe
host
hotly
hound
housebroken
hula
humid
humor
humorous
hutch
hymn
hymnbook

I

ignite
ignore
Illinois
illness
impact
impatience
impossible
improvement
incision
incite
incorrect
indecent
informal
injustice
inn
inner
insane
installment
insult
insurance
insure
intelligence
intelligent
intensely
interest
interesting
invest
investment
invitation
Iowa
ironmaster
issue
itchy

J

jag
jagged
Jamestown
jellybean
jersey
jewel
jeweler
jig
jiggle
Jimmy
joyfully
jungle
justice

K

Karen
keen
keenly
kennel
Kenneth
kettle

keyhole
kidney
kindly
kitten
knothole
knuckle

L
ladder
lain
language
lantern
lattice
lawsuit
lease
lecture
length
lettuce
license
lightheaded
lily
lion
litter
litterbug
Little Rock
livestock
loafer
loan shark
locket
loin
London
lonesome
loop
loophole
loot
looter
Los Angeles
lotion
loudmouth
Louis
lounge
lowland
Lucy
lumber
lumpiness
lumpy
lye
lynch
Lynn(e)

M
madam
madhouse
magical
Maine
mama
manage

mane
mansion
mare
Margaret
margin
marker
market
marketplace
marriage
Mars
marsh
marshmallow
marshy
Maryland
Massachusetts
master
mattress
mayonnaise
meaningful
meantime
mellow
member
Memphis
mental
mercy
metal
Miami
microphone
Midas
middleweight
mill
mindful
miscall
mission
mister
mixed
moneybags
monthly
moral
moreover
Moscow
moth
mothball
motherless
motion
mount
mouthpiece
mummy
music
musical
mustard
mutt
mystery

N
Nancy
napkin

nation
navy
naw
necessary
necklace
needle
needn't
Neil
New Jersey
nickel
niece
nightgown
nightmare
Nile
nit
nitwit
northeastern
northern
nosebleed
nutmeg
nylon

O
oarlock
oath
obey
oblong
obtain
occasion
odds
oily
ointment
Olson
omen
omit
opening
opportunity
orderly
organ
otherwise
outburst
outcry
outdoor
outfielder
outlaw
overjoyed
overpaid
overtook

P
package
pal
palace
Pan
panel
panhandle
panhandler

panic
pantry
parcel
pardon
parent
Paris
parrot
parson
partner
passion
pastime
patience
pavement
payroll
peak
peddler
pencil
per cent
perfect
perfume
permission
permit
persist
personal
perspire
pester
petal
pettiness
petty
phantom
pharmacy
phase
Phil
Philadelphia
Philip
photo
photo finish
photocopy
photograph
photographer
photography
phrase
Phyllis
physic
physical
physician
physique
physics
pickup
piecework
pigsty
pillowcase
pirate
placement
plainclothes
planter

platform
plastic
playmate
playpen
playroom
pleasure
pliers
plop
pluck
plumber
ply
plywood
pocketbook
poem
poet
poise
poisoner
poisonous
polite
pore
porter
pose
possible
post
postcard
postman
postmark
postmaster
potholder
pothole
potpie
powder
power
powerful
powerhouse
prank
precise
predict
prepare
prescribe
presently
pressure
prevent
preview
prick
priest
prime
princess
prison
private
prod
producer
project
promoter
promotion
prophet

prowl
prowler
public
publish
puddle
pulley
pullover
punchy
punish
puppet
puppy
purple
puzzle
Pyrex

Q
quicksand
quietly
quiz

R
rabbit
railing
rainfall
Ralph
ranch
rancher
ransom
rap
rattle
rattlesnake
reaction
ready-made
ready-to-wear
realize
rebirth
reborn
receipt
recent
recess
recite
recline
recognize
recorder
recycle
reed
refer
refreshment
regardless
regret
relationship
relative
relief
relieve
reload
reminder

remission
reorder
replace
replacement
repress
rescue
restore
restrain
reverse
review
revolve
revolver
reward
ribbon
riddle
rightful
rind
ringleader
ringmaster
ringworm
roadside
roam
Rocco
rocket
Rolls Royce
roomful
roominess
roomy
roost
rooster
root
roughly
ruby
rudely
Russia
rye

S
safety
saint
saintly
saleswoman
salute
sandal
scab
scalp
scandal
scarce
scarcely
scarlet
scatter
schoolhouse
schoolroom
schoolteacher
schooner
scoot

Scotland
scoutmaster
scramble
scrapbook
scrawl
screwball
scribble
Scripture
sculpture
scum
Seattle
section
seldom
selection
self-pity
seller
senseless
sensitive
sermon
service
setup
sh!
shabby
shall
shallow
shampoo
sharpen
shed
sheepish
shipshape
shirk
shiver
shoe
shoehorn
shoelace
shoestring
shoplifting
shortchange
shortcoming
shorthand
shortly
showroom
shriek
shrine
shrivel
shrubbery
shrunken
shudder
shyness
sickness
sideline
sidestep
sideswipe
sidetrack
signal
silver

silverware
silvery
singsong
sissy
sister-in-law
situation
sixth
sketchbook
sketchy
skillet
skim
skimp
skit
skitter
slack
slash
slate
slick
slightly
slime
sliminess
slimy
slingshot
slit
slope
sloppiness
slosh
slug
slugger
slumber
slur
smallpox
smelly
smirk
smock
smother
smuggle
smuggler
snack bar
snare
snazzy
snipe
sniper
snippy
snitch
snowflake
snowy
snuff
soccer
socket
Solly
solo
solve
somehow
somewhere
son-in-law

sorehead
sorrow
sorrowful
soul
southern
southwestern
soy
spar
spareribs
sparkle
sparrow
spearmint
speedway
spellbound
spike
spiny
splashdown
splashy
splatter
splendid
splendidly
splotch
splutter
sponsor
spotted
spotty
sprang
sprig
springtime
sprinkle
spruce
sprung
spun
spur
spurt
squad
squash
squawk
squeamish
squid
stab
stack
stag
stagger
stark
startle
steadiness
steady
steeple
stench
stepladder
stern
stickiness
stiff
stock
stole

stolen
stoplight
storage
stormy
storybook
straightforward
strangely
strangle
strangler
strengthen
strep
stretcher
stride
strikeout
stringy
strive
structure
strut
Stuart
stub
stumble
sty
style
stylish
stylus
suggest
suggestion
sunbather
supper
surfer
surround
survive
Susan
swank
sway
sweat shirt
sweetheart
sweetly
swelling
swimsuit
switchblade
swollen
swore
symptom
synonym
system

T
tackle
talkative
talker
tangle
tango
target
taskmaster
tasteful

taut
taxi
teakettle
teamwork
tearfully
teen
teenage
teenager
telephone
tempt
tender
tenderfoot
tenderness
Tennessee
tension
tenth
terror
thank you
thatched
thee
theirs
theme
thereabout
thereafter
they'd
they'll
thickness
thigh
thirteenth
Thor
thorough
thoroughly
thoughtfully
thoughtfulness
thoughtlessness
thrash
thresh
thresher
thriller
throttle
throwaway
thrust
thruway
ticket
tickle
ticklish
tidy
tinkle
toad
tobacco
toilet
toll
tollbooth
toothless
torch
totally

tract
trade-in
traffic
train wreck
traitor
treason
treasure
treasurer
treatment
treaty
trench
trespass
trespasser
tricycle
trigger
trio
trophy
troublesome
trumpet
tumble
tummy
tunnel
turnip
turnpike
twang
tweed
tweezers
twentieth
twig
twirl
twitch
type
typewriter
typewritten
typist

U
umpire
unaffected
unbelievable
uncle
underfoot
unemployed
unequal
uniform
unimportant
unlighted
unlock
unmarried
unnecessary
unpin
unseen
unsteady
unsuccessful
unsuited
upland

urge
urgent
urgently
usher
Utah

V
vacation
vain
Valentine
valley
value
vampire
vanish
vast
vat
vault
veil
velvet
vent
Vermont
version
vet
veteran
veterinarian
veto
vision
volley
volleyball
vulture

W
wail
walnut
walrus
warden
ware
warehouse
Washington, D.C.
watchdog
weakness
wealth
wealthy
wedlock
welcome
welfare
well-to-do
wept
western
we've
wheelchair
whereabouts
where's
whiner
whiplash
whirlpool

whisper
whistle
White House
whoop
whop
whopper
wick
wiggle
wiggly
wildfire
willful
willingness
windpipe
wisdom
wishbone
wishy-washy
wit
withdraw
witness
witty
woodchuck
wooden
workman
wrestle
wrestler
wrinkle

X
x-ray

Y
yank
yearbook
yeast
yep
yoke
yours
youth

Z
zebra
zero
zigzag

a
able
about
above
absent
accept
accident
according
ace
ache
acre
across
act
action
active
actor
A.D.
ad
Adams
add
address
admire
admission
admit
Adolf
adult
advance
advantage
advice
Aesop
affect
afford
afraid
Africa
after
afternoon
afterward
again
against
age
ago
agree
agreement
ah
ahead
ahoy
aid
ail
aim
ain't
air
airplane
airtight
aisle
Al
alarm

alive
all
allow
all right
all-star
almost
alone
along
alongside
aloud
alphabet
already
also
altar
alter
although
always
am
A.M.
ambush
amen
America
American
among
amount
Amsterdam
amuse
amusement
an
and
Andy
anger
angry
animal
ankle
Ann(e)
Annabel
annoy
another
answer
ant
antonym
any
anybody
anyhow
anymore
anyone
anything
anyway
anywhere
apart
apartment
ape
apiece
applaud
applause

apple
applesauce
appoint
appointment
April
are
area
aren't
argue
argument
arise
Arizona
arm
armchair
armful
armpit
army
arose
around
arrest
arrive
arrow
art
artery
as
ash
ashtray
Asia
aside
ask
asleep
at
ate
Atlanta
Atlantic
Atlantic City
atmosphere
attack
attend
attic
August
aunt
author
auto
automobile
autumn
avenue
avoid
awake
aware
away
awful
awfully
awoke
ax(e)
babe

baby
babysit
babysitter
Bacchus
back
backbone
backfire
background
backpack
backrest
backside
backtrack
backward
backwoods
backyard
bacon
bacteria
bad
badge
badly
bag
bagful
baggage
baggy
bagpipe
bail
bait
bake
baker
bakery
bald
ball
balloon
Baltimore
Bambino
ban
band
bang
banjo
bank
banker
banner
banns
baptize
bar
barbecue
barbed
barber
bare
barefoot
barely
barge
bark
barn
Bart
bartender

base
baseball
basement
basin
basket
basketball
bat
batch
bath
bathe
bathing
bathmat
bathrobe
bathroom
bathtub
batter
battered
battery
battle
battleground
battleship
bawl
B.C.
be
beach
bead
beam
bean
bear
beard
beast
beat
beaten
beating
beautiful
beautifully
beauty
became
because
become
bed
bedding
bedroom
bedspread
bedtime
bee
beech
beef
beeline
been
beep
beer
beet
before
beg
began

beggar
begin
beginner
beginning
begun
behalf
behave
behind
belief
believe
believer
bell
bellhop
belly
belong
belonging
below
belt
Ben
bench
bend
bender
beneath
bent
Bergman
berry
berserk
beside
besides
best
bet
Bethlehem
better
between
beyond
bib
Bible
bicycle
bid
bidder
bidding
big
bigwig
bike
bile
bill
billfold
billing
billion
billionth
Billy
bin
bind
binge
bingo
birch

bird
birdhouse
birth
birthday
birthplace
birthstone
bit
bitch
bite
bitten
bitter
blab
black
blackbird
blackboard
blackmail
blacksmith
blacktop
blade
blame
blank
blanket
blankly
blare
blast
blaze
bleach
bleacher
bleed
blend
blender
bless
blessed
blessing
blew
blight
blimp
blind
blindly
blindness
blink
blob
block
blond(e)
blood
bloodhound
bloodshed
bloodshot
bloodstain
bloodstream
bloodthirsty
bloody
bloom
blouse
blow
blowout

blowpipe
blown
blowtorch
blubber
blue
blueberry
blue jay
blues
bluff
blur
blurt
blush
board
boarder
boardwalk
boast
boastful
boat
Bob
Bobby
bobcat
bobsled
bodily
body
bodyguard
boil
boiler
bold
boldness
bolt
bomb
bond
bone
bonnet
bony
book
bookcase
bookmark
bookshelf
bookstore
bookworm
boom
boost
boot
booth
booty
booze
bop
border
bore
boring
born
borrow
boss
bossy
Boston
both
bother

bottle
bottom
bought
bounce
bouncer
bouncy
bound
bout
bow
bowl
bowling
box
boxcar
boxer
boxing
boy
boycott
boyfriend
Boy Scout
brace
bracelet
bracket
Brady
brag
braid
Braille, L.
brain
brainy
brake
branch
brand
brand-new
brandy
brat
brave
bravely
breach
bread
breadboard
breadbox
breadwinner
break
breakdown
breakfast
breakthrough
breast
breath
breathe
breather
breathing
breathless
breed
breeze
breezy
brew
bribe
brick
bride

bridge
bright
brighten
brightly
brightness
brim
bring
brink
brisk
briskly
British
brittle
broil
broiler
broke
broken
brood
brook
broom
broomstick
broth
brother
brotherhood
brother-in-law
brotherly
brought
brow
brown
brownie
bruise
brush
brushoff
bubble
buck
bucket
Bucky
bud
buddy
budge
budget
bug
buggy
build
building
built
bulb
bulk
bulky
bull
bullet
bully
bum
bumble
bump
bumper
bumpy
bun
bunch

bunk
bunny
bunt
burden
burglar
burglary
burn
burner
burnt
burp
burst
bury
bus
bush
bushy
busily
business
businessman
bust
busy
busybody
but
butch
butter
buttercup
butterfingers
butterfly
buttermilk
butterscotch
button
buttonhole
buy
buyer
buzz
buzzer
by
bye
bye-bye
bypass
bystander
cab
cabbage
cabin
cabinet
cactus
cafe
cage
cake
calf
California
call
calm
calmly
came
camel
camp
camper
campground

camping
can
cancer
candle
candy
cane
cannot
can't
canteen
cap
cape
Cape Cod
capital
capitalize
capture
car
carbon
carbon dioxide
card
cardboard
care
career
careful
carefully
careless
carelessly
carelessness
carfare
cargo
Carl
carload
carpenter
carpet
carrot
carry
cart
carton
cartoon
carve
Carver, G. W.
carving
case
cash
cask
casket
cast
castor oil
cat
catbird
catcall
catch
catcher
catchy
category
catfish
Catholic
cattle
catty

caught
cause
caution
cautious
cautiously
cave
caveman
cease
ceasefire
ceaseless
ceiling
celebrate
cell
cellar
census
cent
center
certain
certainly
chain
chair
chairman
chalk
chalkboard
champ
champagne
chance
change
channel
chant
chap
chapel
character
charcoal
charge
Charles
charm
chart
chase
chat
chatter
chatterbox
cheap
cheaply
cheapskate
cheat
check
checkbook
checkers
check-out
checkup
cheek
cheekbone
cheer
cheerful
cheerfully
Cheerios
cheerleader

cheery
cheese
cheeseburger
cheesecake
chef
chemical
cherry
chess
chessboard
chest
chestnut
chew
Chicago
chick
chicken
child
childhood
childish
children
chill
chilly
chin
chip
chirp
chock
chocolate
choice
choke
choose
chooser
choosy
chop
choppy
chopstick
chore
chose
chosen
chow
Chris
Christ
christen
Christian
Christ-like
Christmas
Christmas Eve
Christopher
chrome
chuck
chuckle
chunk
church
churn
cider
cigar
cigarette
cinch
Cincinnati
cinder

Cinderella	cloudburst	comma	convince	cram	cud	day-care
cinnamon	cloudless	command	cook	cramp	cuddle	daydream
circle	cloudy	commander	cookbook	cranberry	cue	daylight
circus	clove	commandment	cooky	crane	cuff	daze
cite	clover	comment	cool	crank	culture	dead
citizen	clown	commission	coolly	crash	cup	deadline
citizenship	club	commit	coon	crate	cupboard	deadlock
city	clubhouse	common	coop	crawl	cupcake	deadly
clack	clue	commonly	cop	crazy	cupful	Dead Sea
claim	clump	commonplace	cope	creak	curb	deaf
clam	clumsily	commotion	copper	creaky	curdle	deafness
clammy	clumsy	compact	copy	cream	cure	deal
clamp	clung	company	copycat	creamy	curfew	dealer
clap	clutch	compare	cord	creature	curl	dear
Clark	clutter	compassion	core	creed	curly	death
clash	coach	compete	cork	creek	curse	deathly
class	coal	complain	corn	creep	curtain	debate
classmate	coast	complaint	corn bread	creepy	curve	debt
classroom	coaster	complete	corner	crept	cuss	decay
clatter	coat	completely	cornstarch	crest	custard	deceased
clause	coating	complex	corny	crevice	custom	December
claw	cob	comply	corpse	crew	customer	decent
clay	cobweb	compose	correct	crib	cut	decently
clean	cock	composed	correctly	cricket	cute	decide
cleaner	cockroach	composer	cost	crime	cutters	decision
cleanse	cocktail	compound	costliness	cripple	cutting	deck
cleanser	cocky	compute	costly	crisp	cycle	declare
clear	cocoa	computer	cot	croak	cyclone	decoy
clearing	coconut	conceal	cotton	crook	dab	deed
clearly	cod	concern	cottonmouth	crooked	dad	deep
cleat	code	concert	couch	crop	daddy	deeply
clench	coffee	concept	cough	cross	daily	deer
clerk	coffeecake	conclude	could	crossbar	Dallas	defeat
Cleveland	coffeepot	condition	couldn't	crossing	dam	defend
click	coffin	conduct	count	crossroad	damage	define
cliff	coil	conductor	countdown	crosswalk	damn	deflate
climate	coin	cone	counter	crouch	damp	degree
climb	Coke	confess	countless	crow	Dan	dejected
clinch	cold	confide	country	crowbar	dance	delicate
cling	cold-blooded	confine	countrymen	crowd	dancer	delicious
clinic	coldly	confirm	countryside	crown	danger	delight
clink	collect	conform	county	crude	dangerous	delightful
clip	collector	confront	courage	crudely	dare	demand
clippers	color	confuse	course	cruel	daring	den
clipping	Colorado	connect	court	cruise	dark	Dennis
clock	colorblind	consent	courthouse	cruiser	darkness	dense
clog	coloring	consonant	courtroom	crumb	darling	dent
close	colt	construct	cousin	crunch	darn	dentist
closely	Columbus	consume	cove	crush	dart	Denver
closeness	comb	consumer	cover	crust	dash	depend
closet	combat	contain	covering	crutch	dashboard	department
clot	combination	container	cow	cry	data	depress
cloth	combine	content	coward	crybaby	date	depression
clothes	come	contest	cowboy	cub	daughter	describe
clothesline	comeback	continue	crab	Cuba	Dave	desert
clothespin	comedown	contract	crack	cube	dawn	deserve
clothing	comfort	control	cracker	Cub Scout	day	desire
cloud	coming	convict	craft	cucumber	daybreak	desk

despite
dessert
destroy
detach
detail
detective
Detroit
devote
diagram
dial
diamond
diary
dice
Dick
dictionary
did
diddle
didn't
die
diet
differ
difference
different
differently
difficult
dig
digest
digestion
digger
dill
dim
dime
dine
diner
dining
dinner
dip
dipper
dipstick
direct
dirt
dirt-cheap
dirty
disable
disagree
disagreement
disappoint
disappointment
disaster
disc
discharge
disclose
discomfort
discount
discourage
discover
discovery
discuss

discussion
disease
diseased
disgrace
disgraceful
disgracefully
disgust
dish
dishpan
dishrag
dishtowel
dishwasher
dishwater
disobey
disorderly
disperse
display
dispose
distress
distressful
distrustful
disturb
ditch
dive
diver
dizzy
do
dock
doctor
dodge
does
doesn't
dog
doggy
dogwood
dollar
dome
done
donkey
don't
doom
door
doorbell
doorknob
doorman
doormat
doorway
dope
dorm
dose
dot
double
doubt
doubtful
dough
doughnut
dove
down

downcast
downfall
downhearted
downhill
downpour
downright
downstairs
downstream
down-to-earth
downtown
downward
doze
dozen
Dr.
draft
drag
drain
drainpipe
drank
drape
draw
drawbridge
drawing
drawn
drawstring
dread
dreadful
dream
dreamer
dreamland
dreamy
dredge
drench
dress
dresser
dressing
dressmaker
dressy
drew
drift
drifter
drill
drink
drip
drive
drive-in
driven
driver
driveway
drone
droop
drop
dropout
drove
drown
drug
druggist
drugstore

drum
drummer
drumstick
drunk
drunken
dry
dryer
duck
duckpin
due
duel
dues
duet
dug
duke
dull
dumb
dumbbell
dummy
dump
dunce
dune
dunk
during
dusk
dust
dusty
Dutch
duty
dye
dying
each
eager
ear
early
earn
earnings
earring
earth
earthquake
ease
easily
easiness
east
Easter
eastern
easy
easygoing
eat
eaten
eater
echo
Eddie
edge
edgewise
edgy
Edison, T.
education

Edward
eel
effect
effort
egg
egghead
eggplant
eggshell
Egypt
eight
eighteen
eighth
eighty
either
elbow
elastic
El Dorado
electric
elephant
eleven
elf
Elizabeth
elk
elm
else
elsewhere
emotion
emotional
employ
empolyee
employer
emptiness
empty
encourage
end
ending
enemy
energy
engage
engine
engineer
England
English
enjoy
enlarge
enough
enter
entire
entirely
envelope
equal
equally
Erie
error
errorless
escape
estate
etc.

eve
even
evening
ever
everglade
evergreen
everlasting
evermore
every
everybody
everyone
everything
everywhere
evil
exact
exactly
example
exceed
except
exchange
excite
excitement
exclaim
exclude
excuse
exercise
exert
exhale
exhaust
exist
existence
expand
expect
expel
expense
expert
explain
explode
explore
explorer
explosion
export
expose
express
expression
ex-slave
extend
extent
extra
extreme
extremely
eye
eyebrow
eyesight
eyestrain
fable
face
fact

factor
factory
fad
fade
fail
faint
faintly
fair
fairly
fairness
fairy
faith
faithful
fake
fall
fallen
false
fame
family
fan
fancy
fang
fantastic
far
faraway
fare
farewell
farm
farmer
farmhouse
farther
fast
fasten
fat
fate
father
fatty
faucet
fault
faultless
faulty
fear
feast
feather
feature
February
fed
fee
feed
feedback
feel
feeler
feeling
feet
fell
fellow
felt
female

fence	flare	fool	freehand	fussy	gig	gong
fender	flash	foolish	freeload	future	giggle	goo
fern	flashlight	foolishly	freely	fuzz	gill	good
fetch	flat	foot	freeway	fuzziness	gin	good-bye
fever	flatfoot	football	freeze	fuzzy	ginger	good-looking
few	flatly	footpath	freezer	gab	gingerbread	goodness
fib	flatten	footprint	freight	gabby	gingerly	good night
fiddle	flatter	footstep	French	gag	gingersnap	goods
fiddler	flattery	footwork	Frenchman	Gail	girl	goof
field	flaw	for	fresh	gaily	girlfriend	goofy
fifteen	flea	forbid	freshly	gain	give	goose
fifteenth	fled	force	freshman	gale	given	gopher
fifty	flee	fore	fret	gall	glad	gorge
fig	fleet	forecast	Friday	gallbladder	gladly	gosh
fight	flesh	forefeet	friend	galley	glance	gossip
fighter	flew	forehead	friendless	gallon	gland	got
figure	flex	forest	friendliness	galoshes	glare	gotten
file	flick	forever	friendly	gamble	glass	gown
fill	flicker	forge	friendship	gambler	glassful	grab
film	flight	forget	fright	game	glaze	grace
filter	flint	forgetful	frighten	gang	gleam	graceful
fin	flip	forgive	frightful	gap	Glen	grade
final	flipper	forgiven	fringe	gape	glider	grain
finally	flirt	forgot	fro	garbage	glitter	grand
find	float	forgotten	frog	garden	glittery	grandchildren
fine	flock	fork	from	gardener	glob	granddaughter
finger	flood	form	front	gargle	globe	grandfather
fingernail	floor	formal	frost	garlic	gloom	grandma
fingerprint	floorboard	former	frostbite	gas	gloomy	grandmother
finish	flop	forth	frosting	gash	glory	grandpa
Finn	floppy	forty	froze	gasp	glove	grandson
fir	Florida	forty-niner	frozen	gate	glow	grandstand
fire	floss	forward	fruit	gauze	glue	granny
firecracker	flour	fought	fruitcake	gave	glum	grant
firelight	flow	found	fruitful	gaze	gnarled	grape
fireplace	flower	fountain	fruitless	gear	gnash	grapefruit
firetrap	flowerpot	four	fruity	gearshift	gnat	graph
firm	flowery	fourteen	fry	gee	gnaw	grasp
firmly	flown	fourth	fudge	geese	gnawing	grass
first	flu	Fourth of July	fuel	gee-whiz	gnome	grasshopper
first aid	flung	fox	full	gem	go	grate
first-rate	flush	foxhole	full-grown	Genesis	goad	grateful
fish	flute	fraction	fully	gent	goal	grave
fishbowl	fly	fracture	fumble	gentle	goat	gravely
fisherman	foam	frail	fume	gentleman	gob	graveyard
fist	foamy	frame	fun	gently	gobble	gravy
fit	fog	France	fund	geography	God	gray
fitness	foggy	frank	funk	George	god	grease
fitting	foil	Frank	funnel	Georgia	goddess	greasy
five	fold	frantic	funny	gerbil	godmother	great
fix	folder	fraud	fur	germ	goes	greatly
flabby	folk	freak	furnish	German	goggles	Greece
flag	folks	Fred	furry	Germany	gold	greed
flake	follow	free	further	get	golden	greedily
flaky	follower	freeborn	fuse	ghost	gold-plated	greediness
flame	fond	freedom	fuss	gift	golf	greedy
flannel	fondly	free-for-all	fussbudget	gifted	golly	Greek
flap	food	freeform	fussiness	gift-wrap	gone	green

greenhouse
Greenland
greens
greet
grew
greyhound
grill
grim
grime
grin
grind
grip
gripe
grizzly
groan
grocery
groin
groom
groove
groovy
grope
grouch
grouchiness
grouchy
ground
group
grow
growl
grown
grownup
growth
grubby
grudge
guard
guess
guest
guide
guilt
guilty
gulf
gull
gully
gulp
gum
gumdrop
gummy
gun
gunner
gunshot
gush
gust
gut
gutter
guy
gym
gymnasium
gyp
gypsy

had
hadn't
hag
hail
hailstone
hailstorm
hair
hairbrush
haircut
hairless
hairpin
hairy
half
half-hour
half-wit
hall
Halloween
halo
halt
ham
hamburger
hammer
hand
handball
handbag
handcuff
handful
handicap
handkerchief
handle
handlebar
handpick
handshake
handsome
handsomely
handwriting
handwritten
handy
hang
hanger
hangover
happen
happily
happiness
happy
harbor
hard
hardly
hardship
hardware
hardworking
harm
harmful
harmless
harness
harp
harsh
Harvey

has
hasn't
haste
hat
hatch
hate
hatless
haul
haunt
haunted
have
haven't
Hawaii
hawk
hay
haymaker
haze
haziness
hazy
he
head
heading
headlight
headline
head-on
headphone
headquarters
headway
heal
health
healthy
heap
hear
heard
hearing
heart
heartbeat
heartbreak
heartfelt
heat
heater
heaven
heaviness
heavy
heavyset
heck
hectic
he'd
heel
height
held
helicopter
hell
he'll
hello
help
helper
helpful

helpless
hem
hen
her
herb
Herb
herd
here
here's
Herman
hero
herself
he's
hey
hi
hid
hidden
hide
hide-and-seek
hideout
high
highchair
high-class
highly
highness
high-priced
high-rise
high school
highway
hike
hiker
hill
him
himself
hind
hint
hip
hire
his
hiss
history
hit
hitch
Hitler, A.
hitless
hitter
hive
hoax
hobby
hobo
hock
hockey
hoist
hold
holder
holdup
hole
holiday

Holland
hollow
Holly
holy
home
homebody
homeland
homeless
homemade
home run
homesick
homework
homey
homonym
honest
honey
honeybee
honeymoon
honk
Honolulu
honor
hood
hook
hooker
hoot
hop
hope
hopeful
hopeless
hopscotch
hormone
horn
hornet
horror
horse
horseback
horseplay
horseshoe
hose
hospital
host
hot
hot dog
hotel
hothouse
hotly
hound
hour
hourglass
hourly
house
housebroken
household
housewife
housework
how
however
how's

hug
huge
huh
hula
hum
human
humid
humor
humorous
hump
humpback
hunch
hundred
hung
hunger
hungry
hunt
hunter
hurl
hurry
hurt
husband
hush
hut
hutch
hymn
hymnbook
I
ice
ice cream
icing
icy
I'd
idea
ideal
if
ignite
ignore
ill
ill-mannered
I'll
Illinois
illness
I'm
immense
impact
impatience
import
important
imported
impose
impossible
impress
improper
improperly
improve
improvement

impure
in
inch
incision
incite
include
income
incorrect
increase
indecent
index
Indian
indoors
infect
infield
inflate
inform
informal
inhale
injure
injury
injustice
ink
inland
inmate
inn
inner
inning
inquest
inquire
insane
insect
inside
insider
insight
insist
inspect
inspector
inspire
installment
instead
instruct
insult
insurance
insure
intelligence
intelligent
intend
intense
intensely
intent
interest
interesting
intermission
intestine
into
invade
invader

invent	jewel	kick	landmark	less	lob	lumpiness
invention	jeweler	kid	landowner	lesson	lobby	lumpy
inventor	jewelry	kidnap	lane	let	lobster	lunch
invest	Jewish	kidney	language	let's	locate	lung
investment	jig	kill	lantern	letter	lock	lunge
invitation	jiggle	killer	lap	lettuce	locker	lurch
invite	Jill	kin	lard	library	locket	lye
involve	Jim	kind	large	lice	lodge	lying
IOU	Jimmy	kindhearted	lark	license	log	lynch
Iowa	Joan	kindly	lash	lick	logger	Lynn(e)
Ireland	job	kindness	last	lid	loin	ma'am
Irish	jobless	kinfolk	latch	lie	London	machine
iron	jog	king	late	life	lone	Mack
ironmaster	jogger	Kirk	lately	lifeboat	loneliness	mad
is	jogging	kiss	later	lifeguard	lonely	madam
island	John	kit	lattice	lifetime	lonesome	made
isn't	Johnson	kitchen	laugh	lift	long	madhouse
issue	join	kite	laughter	light	longing	madly
it	joint	kitten	laundromat	lighten	look	magic
Italy	joke	kitty	laundry	lighter	loop	magical
itch	joker	knack	law	lightheaded	loophole	maid
itchy	Jones	knapsack	lawful	lighthouse	loose	mail
item	jot	knee	lawn	lightly	loosen	mailbox
its	joy	kneecap	lawsuit	like	loot	mailman
it's	Joyce	knee-deep	lawyer	likely	looter	main
itself	joyful	kneel	lay	lily	lord	Maine
I've	joyfully	knelt	layer	limb	Los Angeles	mainly
ivy	judge	knew	laziness	lime	lose	make
jab	jug	knickknack	lazy	limit	loss	make-believe
jack	juice	knife	lead	limp	lost	maker
Jack	juicy	knight	leader	Linda	lot	male
jacket	July	knit	leaf	line	lotion	mall
jackhammer	jump	knob	leafy	liner	loud	malt
jackknife	jumper	knock	league	lining	loudly	mama
jackpot	jumpy	knockout	leak	line-up	loudmouth	mammal
jag	June	knot	leaky	link	Louis	man
jagged	jungle	knothole	lean	lint	Louise	manage
jail	junk	knotty	leap	lion	lounge	manager
jam	jury	know	leapfrog	lip	lousy	mane
James	just	known	learn	lipstick	love	mankind
Jamestown	justice	knuckle	learner	liquid	lovely	manner
January	jut	lab	lease	list	lover	manners
Japan	Karen	lace	leash	listen	low	Mansfield
jar	Kate	lack	least	lit	lowdown	mansion
jaw	keel	lacy	leather	litter	lower	many
jazz	keen	ladder	leave	litterbug	lowland	map
jeans	keenly	lady	lecture	little	loyal	march
jeep	keep	ladybug	led	Little Rock	loyally	March
jeer	keeper	lake	ledge	live	loyalty	mare
Jello	keg	laid	Lee	lively	luck	Margaret
jelly	kennel	lain	left	liver	luckily	margin
jellybean	Kenneth	lamb	lefthanded	livestock	lucky	mark
jerk	kept	lame	leg	living	Lucy	Mark
Jerome	ketchup	lamp	lemon	load	lug	marker
jersey	kettle	lance	lend	loaf	Luke	market
Jesus	key	land	length	loafer	lukewarm	marketplace
jet	keyboard	landlady	lent	loan	lumber	marriage
Jew	keyhole	landlord	Lent	loan shark	lump	marry

Mars
marsh
marshmallow
marshy
Martha
Martin
Mary
Maryland
mash
mask
mass
Massachusetts
master
mat
match
matchbook
mate
math
matter
Matthew
matting
mattress
may
May
maybe
Mayflower
mayonnaise
M.D.
me
meadow
meal
mealtime
mean
meaning
meaningful
meant
meantime
meat
meatball
meatless
medicine
meet
meeting
mellow
melt
member
Memphis
men
mend
mental
mention
menu
mercy
merge
merging
mess
message
messy

met
metal
meteor
meteorite
Miami
mice
Michigan
microphone
Midas
middle
middle-aged
middleweight
midmorning
midnight
Midwest
might
mighty
Mike
mild
mildly
mile
milk
milkshake
mill
million
mince
mincemeat
mind
mindful
mine
miner
mining
mint
minute
mirror
miscall
miscount
misfit
misjudge
misplace
miss
mission
misspell
mist
mistake
mistaken
mister
mistreat
mistrust
mitt
mix
mixed
moan
mob
mock
moist
moisten
mold

moldy
mom
moment
mommy
Monday
money
moneybags
monkey
monkeyshines
month
monthly
mood
moodiness
moody
moon
moonlight
moonshine
moose
mop
mope
moral
more
moreover
morning
Moscow
most
mostly
motel
moth
mothball
mother
motherless
motion
mound
mount
mountain
mouse
mousetrap
mousy
mouth
mouthful
mouthpart
mouthpiece
move
movement
movie
mow
mower
Mr.
Mrs.
Ms.
much
mud
muddy
muffin
mug
mugger
muggy

mule
mummy
munch
murder
murderer
murmur
muscle
muse
museum
music
musical
must
mustard
mustn't
mute
mutt
my
myself
mystery
nag
nail
name
Nancy
nap
napkin
narrow
narrowly
nasty
nation
nature
naughty
navy
naw
near
nearby
nearly
neat
neatly
necessary
neck
necklace
necktie
nectar
need
needle
needless
needn't
needy
neighbor
neighborhood
Neil
neither
nerve
nervous
nervously
nervy
nest
net

never
nevertheless
new
newcomer
New England
New Hampshire
New Jersey
news
newscast
newsletter
newspaper
newsreel
newsstand
New Year's Day
New Year's Eve
New York
New York City
next
nice
nick
nickel
nickname
niece
night
nightclub
nightgown
nightmare
Nile
nine
nineteen
ninety
nip
nit
nitwit
no
nobody
nod
noise
noisily
noisy
none
nonsense
nook
noon
no one
noose
nope
nor
normal
normally
north
NorthAmerica
northeastern
northern
North Pole
Norway
nose
nosebleed

nostril
nosy
not
notch
note
notebook
nothing
notice
November
now
nowhere
nude
nudge
numb
number
nurse
nut
nutmeg
nutty
nylon
oak
oar
oarlock
oat
oath
oatmeal
obey
object
oblong
obtain
occasion
ocean
o'clock
October
odd
oddly
odds
of
off
offer
office
officer
often
oh
Ohio
oil
oily
ointment
okay
old
Olson
omen
omit
on
once
one
one-celled
one-fourth

one-half
one-third
only
onion
onto
ooze
open
opening
opium
opportunity
opposite
or
orange
order
orderly
organ
other
otherwise
ouch
ought
ounce
our
ours
ourselves
out
outburst
outcome
outcry
outdoor
outdoors
outer
outfield
outfielder
outhouse
outlaw
outline
outlook
outnumber
outside
outsider
outskirts
outsmart
outstanding
oven
over
overall
overalls
overboard
overcoat
overcome
overcrowd
overdone
overdraw
overflow
overgrown
overhanging
overhead
overheard

overjoyed
overload
overlook
overnight
overpaid
overseas
overtime
overtook
overturn
overweight
owe
own
owner
ox
oxen
oxygen
oyster
pace
pacemaker
pack
package
pact
pad
padding
paddle
padlock
page
paid
pail
pain
painful
painless
paint
paintbrush
painter
painting
pair
pal
palace
pale
palm
pan
Pan
pancake
pancreas
pane
panel
panhandle
panhandler
panic
pant
pantry
pants
panty
paper
parcel
pardon
parent

Paris
park
parrot
parson
part
partner
party
pass
passbook
passion
Passover
passport
password
past
paste
pastime
pasty
pat
patch
path
patience
patter
pattern
patty
Paul
pause
pave
pavement
paving
paw
pawn
pay
paycheck
payday
payment
payroll
pea
peace
peaceful
peacefully
peach
peak
peanut
pear
pearl
Pearl Harbor
peck
peddler
peek
peel
peeler
peep
peer
pen
pencil
penny
people
pep

pepper
peppy
per
per cent
perch
perfect
perform
performer
perfume
perhaps
period
perk
permission
permit
persist
person
personal
perspire
pest
pester
pet
petal
Peter
pettiness
petty
phantom
pharmacy
phase
Phil
Philadelphia
Philip
phone
phony
photo
photocopy
photo finish
photograph
photographer
photography
phrase
Phyllis
physic
physical
physician
physique
physics
piano
pick
pickle
pickup
picnic
picture
pie
piece
piecework
pig
piggy
piggyback

pigpen
pigsty
pigtail
pile
pill
pillow
pillowcase
pin
pinch
pine
Ping-Pong
pink
Pinocchio
pint
pipe
pipeline
pirate
pit
pitch
pitcher
pitchfork
pity
place
placement
plain
plainclothes
plainly
plan
plane
planet
plant
planter
plastic
plate
platform
platter
play
player
playground
playmate
playpen
playroom
plea
plead
pleasant
please
pleased
pleasing
pleasure
pledge
plenty
pliers
plop
plot
plow
pluck
plug
plum

plumber
plump
plunge
plural
plus
ply
plywood
P.M.
poach
pocket
pocketbook
pocketknife
pod
poem
poet
point
pointless
poise
poison
poisoner
poisonous
poke
poker
Poland
pole
police
policeman
polite
pollen
polo
pond
pool
poor
poorhouse
poorly
pop
popcorn
Pope
porch
pore
pork
port
porter
pose
possible
post
postcard
postman
postmark
postmaster
pot
potato
potato chip
potholder
pothole
potpie
potty
pouch

pounce
pound
pour
pout
powder
power
powerful
powerhouse
practice
praise
prance
prank
pray
prayer
preach
preacher
precise
predict
prepare
prescribe
present
presently
president
press
pressure
pretend
pretty
pretzel
prevent
preview
price
priceless
prick
pride
priest
prime
prince
princess
print
printer
prison
private
prize
probably
problem
process
prod
produce
producer
program
project
promoter
promotion
prompt
promptly
prong
proof
prop

proper
properly
property
prophet
protect
proud
proudly
prove
prowl
prowler
prune
pry
pub
public
publish
puddle
Pueblo
puff
puffy
pull
pulley
pullover
pulse
pump
punch
punchy
punish
punk
punt
puppet
puppy
purple
purr
purse
push
put
putty
puzzle
Pyrex
quack
quart
quarter
quarterback
queen
queer
question
quick
quickly
quicksand
quiet
quietly
quit
quite
quiz
quote
rabbit
race
rack

racket
radio
raft
rag
rage
ragged
raid
rail
railing
railroad
railway
rain
rainbow
raincoat
rainfall
rainstorm
rainy
raise
rake
Ralph
ram
ramp
ran
ranch
rancher
rang
range
rank
ransom
rap
rare
rarely
rash
rat
rate
rattle
rattlesnake
raw
ray
reach
react
reaction
read
reader
reading
ready
ready-made
ready-to-wear
real
realize
really
rear
reason
rebirth
reborn
recall
receipt
receive

recent
recess
recipe
recite
recline
recognize
record
recorder
recover
recovery
recycle
red
reduce
reed
reel
refer
reflect
reform
refresh
refreshment
refrigerator
refund
refuse
regard
regardless
regret
reject
rejection
rejoice
relate
relationship
relative
relax
release
relief
relieve
reload
remain
remains
remark
remember
remind
reminder
remission
remove
renew
rent
reorder
repaid
repair
repeat
replace
replacement
reply
report
reporter
repress
request

require
rescue
respect
respectful
respond
rest
restaurant
restless
restore
restrain
restroom
result
retire
retreat
return
reveal
reverse
review
revive
revolve
revolver
reward
rewrite
rhyme
rib
ribbon
rice
rich
rid
ridden
riddle
ride
ridge
rig
rigging
right
rightful
righthanded
rim
rind
ring
ringleader
ringmaster
ringside
ringworm
rinse
rip
ripe
rise
risen
risk
risky
river
road
roadside
roadwork
roam
roar

roast
rob
robber
robbery
robe
Rocco
rock
rocket
rocky
rod
rode
role
roll
roller
Rolls Royce
Rome
roof
room
roomful
roominess
roomy
roost
rooster
root
rope
rose
rosebud
rosy
rot
rotten
rough
roughly
round
route
row
rowboat
Roy
royal
royally
royalty
rub
rubber
ruby
rude
rudely
rug
rule
ruler
run
rung
runner
runny
runt
rush
Russia
rust
rusty
rut

Ruth
rye
sack
sad
sadly
sadness
safe
safely
safety
said
sail
sailor
saint
saintly
sake
salad
sale
salesman
saleswoman
saliva
salt
salty
salute
Sam
same
sample
sand
sandal
sandpaper
sandwich
sandy
sang
sank
Santa Claus
sat
Saturday
sauce
saucepan
saucer
save
savings
saw
say
saying
says
scab
scald
scale
scalp
scaly
scandal
scar
scarce
scarcely
scare
scarecrow
scarf
scarlet

scary
scatter
scheme
school
schoolhouse
schoolroom
schoolteacher
schooner
scold
scoop
scoot
scorch
score
scoreboard
scotch
Scotch
Scotland
Scott
scour
scout
scoutmaster
scram
scramble
scrap
scrapbook
scrape
scraper
scratch
scratchy
scrawl
scream
screech
screen
screw
screwball
screwdriver
scribble
scribe
script
Scripture
scroll
scrounge
scrub
scruff
sculpture
scum
sea
seacoast
seafood
seal
seaport
search
season
seat
Seattle
seaweed
second
section

see
seed
seek
seem
seen
seep
seldom
selection
self
selfish
self-pity
sell
seller
semi-
send
sense
senseless
sensitive
sent
sentence
September
sermon
serve
service
set
setting
settle
setup
seven
seventeen
seventh
seventy
several
sex
sh!
shabby
shack
shade
shady
shaggy
shake
shaken
shaker
shaky
shall
shallow
shame
shameful
shampoo
shape
share
shark
sharp
sharpen
sharply
shatter
shave
she

shed
she'd
sheep
sheepish
sheepskin
sheer
sheet
shelf
shell
shelter
she's
shift
shine
shiny
ship
shipshape
shipwreck
shirk
shirt
shiver
shock
shoe
shoehorn
shoelace
shoestring
shook
shoot
shop
shoplifting
shopper
shopping
shore
short
shortcake
shortchange
shortcoming
shortcut
shorthand
shortly
shorts
shortstop
shot
shotgun
should
shoulder
shouldn't
shout
shove
show
shower
shown
showoff
showroom
shrank
shred
shriek
shrill
shrimp

shrine
shrink
shrivel
shrub
shrubbery
shrug
shrunk
shrunken
shudder
shut
shy
shyly
shyness
sick
sickness
side
sideline
side show
sidestep
sideswipe
sidetrack
sidewalk
sideways
sift
sigh
sight
sign
signal
silent
silk
silky
sill
silly
silver
silverware
silvery
simple
sin
since
sinful
sing
singe
singer
single
singsong
singular
sink
sip
sir
sissy
sister
sisterhood
sister-in-law
sit
sitter
situation
six
six-shooter

sixteen
sixth
sixty
size
skate
skater
sketch
sketchbook
sketchy
ski
skid
skill
skillet
skillful
skim
skimp
skin
skinny
skip
skipper
skirt
skit
skitter
skull
skunk
sky
skylight
skyline
skyscraper
slack
slacks
slam
slang
slant
slap
slash
slate
slaughter
slave
sled
sleep
sleepily
sleepless
sleepy
sleet
sleeve
sleeveless
sleigh
slept
slice
slick
slid
slide
slight
slightly
slim
slime
sliminess

slimy
sling
slingshot
slip
slipper
slit
slop
slope
sloppiness
sloppy
slosh
slot
slouch
slow
slowdown
slowly
slowpoke
slug
slugger
slum
slumber
slump
slung
slur
slush
sly
smack
small
smallpox
smart
smash
smear
smell
smelly
smile
smirk
Smith
smock
smog
smoggy
smoke
smoker
smoky
smooth
smoothly
smother
smudge
smuggle
smuggler
snack
snack bar
snag
snail
snake
snakebite
snap
snapper
snappy

snapshot
snare
snarl
snatch
snazzy
sneak
sneakers
sneaky
sneeze
sniff
snip
snipe
sniper
snippy
snitch
snob
snore
snow
snowball
snowflake
snowplow
snowstorm
snowy
snuff
so
soak
soap
soapy
soar
sob
soccer
sock
socket
socks
soda
soft
softly
soil
sold
sole
solid
Solly
solo
solve
some
somebody
somehow
someone
something
sometimes
somewhat
somewhere
son
song
son-in-law
soon
sore
sorehead

sorrow
sorrowful
sorry
sort
sought
soul
sound
soundly
soup
soupspoon
sour
sourball
sourpuss
south
South America
southern
southpaw
South Pole
southwest
southwestern
sox
soy
space
spade
spaghetti
Spain
span
spangle
spank
spar
spare
spareribs
spark
sparkle
sparrow
speak
speaker
spear
spearmint
speck
sped
speech
speechless
speed
speedily
speedway
speedy
spell
spellbound
spelling
spend
spendthrift
spent
spice
spicy
spider
spike
spill

spin
spine
spiny
spit
spite
spiteful
splash
splashdown
splashy
splatter
spleen
splendid
splendidly
splint
splinter
split
splotch
splurge
splutter
spoke
spoken
spoil
sponsor
spoon
spoonful
sponge
spongy
sport
spot
spotless
spotted
spotty
spout
sprain
sprang
sprawl
spray
spread
sprig
spring
springtime
sprinkle
sprint
sprout
spruce
sprung
spun
spur
spurt
spy
squad
square
squarely
squash
squawk
squeak
squeaky
squeal

squeamish	sticky	strike	sunburn	swollen	Ted	they'll
squeeze	stiff	strikeout	Sunday	swore	tee	they're
squid	still	string	sundown	sworn	teen	they've
squirm	sting	string bean	sunflower	swung	teenage	thick
squirrel	stink	stringy	sung	syllable	teenager	thicken
squirt	stir	strip	sunglasses	symptom	teepee	thickly
squish	stitch	stripe	sunk	synonym	teeth	thickness
stab	stock	strive	sunken	system	telephone	thief
stack	stocking	stroke	sunless	tab	television	thigh
stadium	stole	stroll	sunlight	table	tell	thin
stag	stolen	strong	sunny	tablecloth	teller	thinner
stage	stomach	strongly	sunrise	tablespoon	temper	thing
stagecoach	stomp	struck	sunset	tack	temperature	think
stage fright	stone	structure	sunshine	tackle	tempt	thinker
stagger	stony	struggle	sunstroke	tag	ten	third
stain	stood	strut	suntan	tail	tend	thirst
stair	stool	Stuart	supper	tailor	tender	thirsty
stairway	stoop	stub	suppose	tailspin	tenderfoot	thirteen
stale	stop	stuck	sure	take	tenderness	thirteenth
stall	stoplight	student	surely	taken	Tennessee	thirty
stamp	storage	study	surf	tale	tennis	this
stand	store	stuff	surfer	talk	tenpin	Thomas
standstill	stork	stuffing	surprise	talkative	tense	Thor
stank	storm	stuffy	surround	talker	tension	thorn
star	stormy	stumble	survive	tall	tent	thorough
starch	story	stunt	Susan	tame	tenth	thoroughly
stare	storybook	stupid	Sutter	tan	term	those
starfish	stove	stutter	swallow	tangle	termite	though
stark	straight	sty	swam	tango	terrible	thought
start	straighten	style	swamp	tank	terror	thoughtful
startle	straightforward	stylish	swank	tap	test	thoughtfully
starve	strain	stylus	sway	tape	Texas	thoughtfulness
stash	strainer	sub	swear	tar	than	thoughtless
state	strand	subject	sweat	target	thank	thoughtlessness
statement	strange	subway	sweater	task	thankful	thousand
station	strangely	success	sweat shirt	taskmaster	Thanksgiving	thrash
stay	stranger	successful	Swede	taste	thank you	thread
steadiness	strangle	successfully	Sweden	tasteful	that	threat
steady	strangler	such	sweep	tasteless	thatched	threaten
steak	strap	suck	sweeper	tasty	that's	three
steal	strapless	sudden	sweet	taught	thaw	thresh
steam	straw	suddenly	sweetheart	taut	the	thresher
steel	strawberry	suds	sweetly	tax	thee	threw
steep	stray	suffer	swell	taxi	theft	thrift
steeple	streak	sue	swelling	tea	their	thrifty
steer	stream	Sue	swept	teach	theirs	thrill
stem	streamline	sugar	swift	teacher	them	thriller
stench	street	sugarless	swiftly	teacup	theme	throat
step	strength	suggest	swim	teakettle	themselves	throb
step-by-step	strenghthen	suggestion	swimmer	team	then	throne
stepladder	strep	suit	swimsuit	teamwork	there	throttle
stern	stress	suitcase	swing	teapot	thereabout	through
Steve	stressful	sulk	swipe	tear	thereafter	throughout
Steven	stretch	sulky	swirl	tearful	therefore	throw
stew	stretcher	sum	Swiss	tearfully	there's	throwaway
stick	strict	summer	switch	tearoom	these	thrown
sticker	strictly	sun	switchblade	tease	they	thrust
stickiness	stride	sunbather	swizzle	teaspoon	they'd	thruway

thud	torch	trophy	unarmed	unsure	vest	wasteful
thumb	tore	trouble	unaware	untie	vet	watch
thump	torn	troublesome	unbelievable	until	veteran	watchdog
thunder	toss	trounce	uncertain	untrained	veterinarian	watcher
Thursday	total	trousers	uncle	unwilling	veto	watchful
thus	totally	trout	unclear	unwrap	vice	watchman
tick	touch	truce	uncommon	up	view	water
ticket	touchdown	truck	uncooked	up-and-down	vine	watery
tickle	tough	trudge	uncover	upcoming	vision	wave
ticklish	toward	true	under	update	visit	wavy
tide	towel	truly	underdog	uphill	voice	wax
tidy	town	trumpet	underdone	upkeep	void	way
tie	townspeople	trunk	underfoot	upland	volley	we
tight	toy	trust	underground	upon	volleyball	weak
tighten	trace	truth	underline	upper	volt	weaken
tightly	track	truthful	underneath	uproar	vote	weakness
tile	tract	truthfully	undershirt	upset	voter	wealth
tilt	trade	try	understand	upside-down	vow	wealthy
Tim	trade-in	tub	understood	upstairs	vowel	wear
time	trader	tube	undertaker	upstate	vulture	weather
tin	traffic	tuck	underwear	uptown	wade	web
tinkle	trail	Tuesday	underworld	upward	wage	wed
tiny	train	tug	undid	urge	wail	wedding
tip	trainer	tumble	undo	urgent	waist	wedlock
tire	training	tummy	undress	urgently	waistline	Wednesday
tissue	train wreck	tune	uneasy	us	wait	weed
to	trait	tuner	unemployed	use	waiter	week
toad	traitor	tunnel	unequal	used	waitress	weekday
toast	tramp	turkey	uneven	useful	wake	weekend
toaster	trance	turn	unfair	useless	walk	weekly
tobacco	trap	turnip	unfit	usher	wall	weep
today	trapper	turnpike	unfold	Utah	wallet	weigh
toe	trash	turtle	unfriendly	utter	walnut	weight
together	trashy	TV	unhappy	vacation	walrus	welcome
toil	tray	twang	unhealthy	vain	Walter	welfare
toilet	tread	tweed	uniform	Valentine	waltz	well
told	treason	tweezers	unimportant	valley	wander	we'll
toll	treasure	twelve	unit	value	want	well-done
tollbooth	treasurer	twentieth	United States	vampire	war	well-known
Tom	treat	twenty	universe	van	warden	well-to-do
tomato	treatment	twice	unlawful	vane	ware	went
Tommy	treaty	twig	unless	vanilla	warehouse	wept
tomorrow	tree	twin	unlighted	vanish	warm	were
ton	treeless	twine	unlikely	vase	warmblooded	we're
tone	trench	twirl	unlock	vast	warn	weren't
tongue	trend	twist	unluckily	vat	warning	west
tonight	trespass	twitch	unlucky	vault	was	western
Tony	trespasser	two	unmade	veal	wash	wet
too	tribe	type	unmarried	vegetable	washbowl	we've
took	trick	typewriter	unmated	veil	washcloth	whack
tool	tricky	typewritten	unnecessary	vein	washer	whale
toolbox	tricycle	typist	unpack	velvet	washing	wham
tooth	trigger	ugly	unpin	vent	Washington	what
toothbrush	trim	ulcer	unsafe	verge	Washington, D.C.	whatever
toothless	trio	umpire	unseen	Vermont	washtub	what's
toothpaste	trip	unable	unsteady	verse	wasn't	whatsoever
top	troop	unaffected	unsuccessful	version	waste	wheat
topping	trooper	unafraid	unsuited	very	wastebasket	wheel

wheelchair
wheeze
wheezy
when
whenever
where
whereabouts
where's
wherever
whether
which
whichever
whiff
while
whim
whine
whiner
whip
whiplash
whirl
whirlpool
whiskey
whisper
whistle
white
White House
who
whoever
whole
whom
whoop
whop
whopper
who's
whose
why
wick
wide
widely
widespread
wife
wig
wiggle
wiggly
wild
wildflower
wilderness
wildfire
wildly
will
willful
William
willing
willingness
wilt
win
wince
wind

window
windpipe
wine
wing
wink
winner
winter
wipe
wiper
wire
wiring
wiry
wisdom
wise
wisecrack
wisely
wish
wishbone
wishful
wishy-washy
wit
witch
with
withdraw
within
without
witness
witty
woke
woman
women
won
wonder
wonderful
won't
wood
woodchuck
wooden
woodpecker
woods
woodwork
woody
wool
woolly
word
wore
work
worker
workman
workshop
world
World War II
worm
worn
worn-out
worry
worse
worship

worst
worth
worthless
worthy
would
wouldn't
wound
wow
wrap
wrapper
wrapping
wreck
wrecker
wren
wrench
wrestle
wrestler
wring
wrinkle
wrist
wristwatch
write
writer
writing
written
wrong
wrote
wrung
x-ray
yank
Yankee
yard
yawn
ye
yeah
year
yearbook
yearly
yeast
yell
yellow
yep
yes
yesterday
yet
Y.M.C.A.
yoga
yogurt
yoke
yolk
you
you'd
you'll
young
your
you're
yours
yourself

youth
you've
yuk
Yule
zebra
zero
zigzag
zip
zipper
zone
zoo

192   Word Index: Books 1-5